The Search for Blonnye Foreman

the absorbing story of a missionary
who found deeper meaning

The Search for
Blonnye
Foreman

.

Jesse C.
Fletcher

Broadman Press / Nashville, Tennessee

To

David and Susie

This book attempts to tell the story of Blonnye Foreman through the eyes of the two missionaries involved. It seeks to be true to the viewpoint of missionary strategy that these men, restricted to specific times and places, would have. Conversations are creatively reconstructed. Some incidental matters of time, place, and circumstance are paraphrased for the normal protection of privacy and other reasons.

Dewey Decimal Classification Number: 266.092
Library of Congress Catalog Card Number: 69-17895
Printed in the United States of America
3.My7014

Acknowledgments

THE SEARCH FOR BLONNYE FOREMAN was carried on with the gracious help of many people. They have certainly made my task easier, but they can in no way be held responsible for the results. Decisions as to treatment of material ultimately were mine alone.

James E. Musgrave, Jr., missionary to Brazil currently stationed in Rio de Janeiro, provided the majority of the data related to the efforts to find Blonnye Foreman. In fact, Musgrave's classic report on the matter could serve as a model for recording the facts on similar events. His helpfulness has been given with thoughtfulness and dedication to the idea that inspiration and renewed commitment to the cause of Christ could result from this search.

Close friends of Blonnye Foreman's also offered much help. J. M. Sibley and his daughter Annita Sibley Frazier, who had done a great deal of research on Blonnye's life, furnished invaluable help. Blonnye's former roommate, N. B. Moon, would fall in the same category, along with Missionary Blanche Simpson. Miss Ruby Atwood of Abilene, Texas, was especially considerate and helpful. Jerry Smyth, also a missionary to Brazil, offered thoughtful criticism, as did Frank Means, area secretary for South America for the Foreign Mission Board.

Because of the peculiar thrust of this narrative, many sources of information known to the author were not consulted. A definitive biography was not the goal.

As in previous literary efforts on my part, my secretary, Marilyn Fairfax Glazebrook; my editor in chief, Genevieve Greer; and my passionately loyal family made the real difference in moving this project from idea to reality.

5

I am aware THE SEARCH FOR BLONNYE FOREMAN does not fit the mold of missionary biography. But then this is the way I saw it.

JESSE C. FLETCHER

Richmond, Virginia
March 5, 1969

Contents

1. April 4, 1955   9

2. 1929   15

3. April 10, 1955   26

4. 1930   32

5. April 13, 1955   43

6. 1934   48

7. April 15, 1955   58

8. 1941   66

9. April 16, 1955   76

10. 1947   83

11. April 18, 1955   94

12. 1952   98

13. April 18, 1955, 9:30 P.M.   107

14. 1953   113

15. April 19, 1955, 3:00 A.M.   123

16. 1955   128

17. April 19, 1955, 5:00 A.M.   141

1
April 4, 1955

(JAMES MUSGRAVE)

The messenger boy boldly pedaled his bike through a puddle left from a recent rain. As the water cascaded around his pedals, he lifted his feet and held the telegram he was carrying high over his head in exaggerated concern for his responsibility.

He slowed to a stop at a neat white stucco house surrounded by a low wall, topped by black wrought iron, and almost totally enveloped by a lush bougainvillea. Deftly dismounting, the messenger pulled the bike to the wall and took a rumpled messenger's cap from his back pocket.

At the door of the house he put on his cap, drew himself up smartly, and knocked.

After the second knock, the door opened and the boy grew wide-eyed at the size of a tall, broad-faced gringo who appeared from the semidarkness of the house that was just coming to life after the hot, still Brazilian night.

"Bom-dia, senhor," the boy said.

"Bom-dia." The man's reply was friendly.

"Telegram for *Senhor* Musgrave." The boy pronounced it "Moosegraf."

"I am James Musgrave."

The boy handed Musgrave the telegram, took a rumpled cruzeiro note in return, smiled with satisfaction, and left.

9

"Who was it, Jim?" The voice of Musgrave's wife came from the kitchen where familiar smells and sounds indicated an impending breakfast.

"A messenger." Musgrave walked into the kitchen where the light was better and opened the cream, official-looking envelope.

Jan Musgrave put a plate of papaya slices on the table and turned to her husband.

"What does it say?"

Musgrave's voice was unsteady as he replied.

"It's from Campos Belos. Blonnye Foreman is missing."

"Missing? In the plane?"

"Yes."

Musgrave stared at the few words on the square of paper as if they would somehow say more.

"Oh, Jim, I hope he's all right."

"He probably just landed somewhere to wait out bad weather and got talked into preaching."

The young missionary spoke with more assurance than he really felt. Inside he was already dealing with a long repressed fear that tragedy would one day overtake the intrepid senior missionary in his small plane.

"What are you going to do?" Jan's voice jarred Musgrave from his shocked silence.

"I guess I'd better make some inquiries. Contact Campos Belos. Maybe I'd better check at the air base. I guess I should go over there. . . ." Musgrave's voice trailed off and then with forced lightness he said, "He's probably back by now, hale and hearty."

"If you call the air base and he's really all right, won't you run the risk of getting him in trouble?"

Both of them remembered a recent round of difficulty with the aviation authorities over an unauthorized night flight Foreman had made. That it had been a mission of mercy to bring a woman desperately ill to medical facilities did not alter the fact he had made an

illegal flight. Brazilian aviation laws specifically forbade single engine planes to fly after sundown.

"Yes, you're right. I guess I should check first in Campos Belos
and make sure he's back. If he's not back, they may have some word
from him."

An hour later Jim Musgrave, nursing an ill-digested breakfast, was
driving down the dusty road that linked Goiana, where Jim lived,
to Anapolis, approximately sixty kilometers away. Blonnye Foreman
was supposed to have been going to Anapolis when he left his base
at Campos Belos. That was all Musgrave had been able to learn.

During the hour that had passed since he received the telegram,
Musgrave had worked hard to alleviate the sense of dread it had pro-
voked. Mile by mile he tried to reassure himself, but his mind seemed
unable to reassure his stomach.

It disturbed him that he knew so little about his fellow missionary.
He was not even sure how old he was—fifty? He always thought
Foreman was a native of New Mexico, but at the last Mission meeting somebody called him an Arkansas farmer. Evidently he had been
born in Arkansas, but had later moved to New Mexico.

Their stations were not that remote. Musgrave realized that with
a little effort on his part they could spend more time together. Perhaps
Foreman's being single accounted for the lack of fellowship. On the
other hand, Foreman, apart from his plane, was isolated at Campos
Belos and their work was fairly distinct. Blonnye had a reputation
for going his own way, stubbornly and good-naturedly.

Musgrave swerved to avoid a car careening down the opposite
side of the narrow Brazilian road. He caught himself evaluating the
other driver's character in Portuguese and decided he was getting
pretty well acclimated to the Brazilian environment.

Methodically, Musgrave tried to pull his wandering thoughts back into an orderly sequence. If he had to report Foreman's plane missing, what could he say?

Let's see, what color was it? Yellow? No, green. That's right, it was green. He remembered seeing it in Goiana. . . . His mind conjured a clear image of Blonnye standing on a ladder pouring gas into the wing tanks through a chamois cloth laid across the opening to filter out impurities. The Campos Belos air strip near Blonnye Foreman's home was a pretty rudimentary affair. And the hangar where he put his plane up—on the rare occasions it was back at the base—was little more than a shed.

The number. What was the number? RT? Musgrave knitted his brow as he tried to remember the number of Foreman's green plane. *PTARM. That was it.* He remembered Foreman calling it his right arm. Despite the fact that missionaries all over Brazil were alarmed at the older missionary's new form of transportation, Foreman had stoutly defended his decision by pointing out that he covered in his plane in three days what it had taken him three months to cover by burro, the way he first pioneered the Goias interior four years before.

The type? Musgrave remembered it had been called a Super Cub. All airplanes had been Piper Cubs to him, but Blonnye had patiently explained to him that this was a Super Cub with more power than the ordinary Piper Cub. Musgrave wasn't sure. He didn't feel real comfortable folding his large frame in the small back seat where Foreman placed him on their one joint trip.

The low adobe buildings alongside the road announced his arrival at the outskirts of Anapolis, a small Brazilian city located on a high plateau and featuring a major airport.

Blonnye might be at the airport having his plane repaired. He had most of his repairs and maintenance done there except for a few things he had done in Sao Paulo a few months before. Strange that a fellow raised on a farm knew so little about combustion engines.

As he thought about it, Musgrave decided this judgment contradicted another piece of information. Had not Blonnye Foreman showed Musgrave a complex and ambitious design for a hydroelectric plant for the Corrente River, near the school where Foreman was stationed the first twenty years of his missionary career? He was going to have to ask Blonnye about things like that, he decided. He would not let himself add the obvious—if he ever saw him again.

"*Senhor* Foreman?" The grease-spattered mechanic whom Musgrave felt sure would know whether or not Foreman had been to Anapolis grinned broadly at the memory.

"Sure, *Senhor* Blonnye was here last week. He fueled his plane and left it overnight. Said he was going to Pirenopolis or maybe it was Corrente. I forget; he flies everywhere."

"I see," said Musgrave. "He's not back at Campos Belos yet and the people up there are kind of worried."

The smile disappeared from the mechanic's face for just a moment. Then he smiled, "*Ai!* he's okay. God takes care of him. He told me so. He says that even in storms or if the motor stops or the wings fall off, God will take care of him.

"He is crazy, that *Senhor* Foreman. But I like him."

Jim Musgrave smiled at the mechanic's happy banter. Foreman did talk a lot about the Almighty's provision for his flying contingencies.

"You think he may have gone to Corrente?" Musgrave inquired further.

"Yes, I think he said he was going to Corrente. He's always talking about his orphan girls and he said he needed some papers for them. But there was also some worker he was to pick up somewhere. Maybe he was to take the worker with him to Corrente. I don't know. I am sure he is all right."

Musgrave thanked the mechanic and walked back to his car.

That's it, he decided, Blonnye's gone to Corrente and there's no way for him to get word from there.

He ticked off in his mind the time it would take to fly to Corrente and the kind of terrain that would be located between Anapolis and Corrente.

With all the friends Blonnye had in the little town where he lived for so many years, he had simply delayed his return.

Too, he may have had to wait on documents for his girls. He had reared them in a home he had established in Corrente.

Musgrave started his car and pulled it thoughtfully into gear. Well, there's no use worrying about it. Such worries had been futile before and he prayed silently they would be futile this time.

He started back down the road to Goiana, going faster than usual, as if to put the uncertainties behind him.

2
1929

(BLONNYE FOREMAN)

On a warm June night in 1929 the sleeping town of Clovis, New Mexico, basked beneath the benevolent serenity of a large bright moon. Dogs, crickets, the noise of an occasional car, and the whisper of a light breeze through the prairie brush furnished an appropriate sound track.

Blonnye Foreman, however, was quite oblivious to all this. Lost in thought, he walked slowly along the railroad track leading out of town. He was a lonely figure, but he was unaware of that, also. His mind was consumed with the arguments and counterarguments, the people for and those against, the reasons to and the reasons not to, the implications and the questions of a man trying to reach a difficult decision.

That God had called him to be a missionary to Brazil, Blonnye did not doubt. He was grateful he would not need to resolve that matter again. Too well he remembered the lonely seventeen-year-old farm boy in Rosebud, Arkansas, struggling so painfully with the uncertainties of what he should do with his life. He remembered another summer night—fifteen years ago now—when he slipped away from his farm home in Rosebud looking for that illusive something. He had still not found it when he returned home a few embarrassed days later.

Maybe this is why there was no grief when his family decided to leave their Arkansas farm and migrate to the high plains of New Mexico. Perhaps he had known instinctively he would find what he was looking for in New Mexico.

Things had fallen into place in his new home. In peaceful sequence he had made a Christian commitment, felt God calling him to be a preacher, and then defined that calling to mean a missionary preacher to Brazil. The final stage had come into focus during his college days at Hardin-Simmons in Abilene, Texas. The memory of that college decision was once more very real. Only a few hours earlier he had gathered with several friends from college days around the hospitable table of Mrs. Laura Buster in Clovis. Mrs. Buster's two daughters were missionaries in Brazil, and she had invited for dinner several like Blonnye who hoped to become missionaries.

Remembering the events of a few hours before, Blonnye stopped on the track and unbuttoned the coat that only a few moments earlier he had stopped to button. The New Mexico breeze bathed his face with a mixture of cool air off the nearby Sangre de Cristo Mountains and warm air residual from the heat of the day. He brushed a wisp of hair from his forehead and readjusted his steel-rimmed glasses.

The five of them gathered around Mrs. Buster's table had applied to the Baptist Foreign Mission Board for appointment as missionaries. All had received the same answer. Not yet. The Board, despite the prosperity of the country, was in deep financial straits and money was not available to send them. Their offers to find their own support or to go independently until such time as the Board could appoint them had been turned aside. Dr. Ray, the executive secretary of the Board, had written each of them counseling them against such "rash" moves.

Setting his jaw, Blonnye remembered that the tone of their conversation that night had run in just that direction—to go ahead, not to ask God to wait until men arrived at their own good times but to go in what seemed to be in God's time. Even a furloughing Brazilian missionary who had met with them that night (and who had formerly counseled them all against independent action), now suggested that it might be the thing to do in light of the Board's indefiniteness as to when funds for appointing new missionaries would be available.

Blonnye started walking again. *But it was not a collective action they were considering. Each person had an individual decision to make.* At this point he knew his problem was not what they should do; his problem was what he ought to do.

Looking up at the star-studded sky, Blonnye stopped once more. If he knew his own heart, he was ready to go. Also, if he knew his own heart, he wanted to do what God wanted him to do even if that meant staying. The letter from the Board's secretary had not made him angry; perhaps he would talk the same way if he were trying to hold together what support he had and did not want to see it milked off in unilateral actions.

He reviewed the plan he had outlined to the group around the table after supper. . . .

"I have $350 in the bank now. Several people have pledged to send me money and I have other gifts promised which should outfit me."

"How much will your passage down there be?" Ruby Atwood had her chin propped in her hand, intensely caught up in his plans.

"About $300," Blonnye replied. "I figure I am going to need about $150 for outfit, however, and then I would like to have enough to be able at least to make it the first few months."

"What about work with our missionaries?"

"Several have said they were sure I could get a job teaching in the school or working in our publishing house in Rio."

"I hear you can almost support yourself by teaching English to Brazilians."

"I have heard that, too," Blonnye said. "Hopefully, I can defray most of my living expenses that way. On the other hand, I do not want to get so tied down making expenses that I can't do what I am going down there to do."

"But isn't your first task going to be to learn Portuguese?"

"That's right, and that's going to take at least a year."

"But what if you can't get a job?" Ruby asked. . . .

Blonnye Foreman stopped on the track, now well out of town, and looked back toward Clovis with its lights blinking in the clear night air. Facing that penetrating question once more, he hardly heard the mournful howl of a coyote farther down the track.

What would he do? Couldn't he trust God for that? He tried to answer his own questions. He knew he could. He knew he simply had to let his weight down on God's promises to take care of him as he tried to do God's will. Surely if God wanted him in Brazil, God would provide for him. Did he not already have assurance of that? Where did the $350 come from if it was not from the providing hand of the same God who had called him to preach?

He walked more briskly now, drawing courage from his own thoughts. Indecision was giving way to something more definite.

Then he stopped again. It was a time for honesty. Was that the full scope of his indecisions: a question of finances, going independent rather than as an appointed missionary? Or was there more?

Only a few days before one of his closest friends had asked him why he did not wait until he had found a wife to go to Brazil.

"Blonnye, you don't dare go into a country like that with the kind of problems you will find there as a single man. You'll need a wife to be a good missionary."

"You haven't got a whole lot of biblical support for that statement," Blonnye replied laughingly. "But I do agree with you. I could probably do a better job in some ways if I were married. But I do not believe God calls a man to marry simply for expediency. I am not going to marry anyone I am not in love with."

"In love with." Blonnye Foreman rammed both hands deep in his pockets as he pondered that phrase—"in love." A man ought to be in love to get married.

But what if he fell in love with somebody whom he could not marry? What if the only love he had experienced in his life was too preposterous even to consider? He had not been able to discuss that question. And even now the situation was too impossible to consider.

No, lack of a mate would not stop him. God could provide for his needs as a single man the same as he could provide for his material needs as an independent missionary.

"But you will not be independent," Ruby had said at the table.

That was true, he thought. He was going to be very dependent upon friends and loved ones—people who believed as he believed. He was going to be dependent upon God.

Others had decided already. Blanche Simpson was going to Brazil on her own, and Floy Hawkins had said she was going to China the same way.

Blonnye Foreman had not said then, but now, as he turned around and started back toward Clovis, he knew he was going to Brazil with whatever God made available and that right soon.

For just a moment a bright moon flirted with a lonesome cloud and seemed to try to mock his resolve, but the assurance of his decision came with renewed determination.

The boat had stopped.

Jumping from his bunk, he reached for the porthole and there spread out before him lay the beauty of Rio de Janeiro. He exulted in the sight of the fabled Brazilian port. Quickly he identified the landmarks he had been over in his mind a hundred times. There was Sugar Loaf. There was Corcovado. Over that way Copacabana. The green mountains ringing the city reached right up into incredibly blue skies and mirrored in occasional shadows the white fluffy clouds that were already gathering in preparation for a later afternoon presentation of rain.

It felt good. This is where God had called him and now he was here. Hurriedly he began to dress. He was almost packed when he realized this was no day to pass up his morning devotions. He took his Bible, sat down at his desk, read almost without understanding, and bowed his head in fervent prayer.

Days succeeded days rapidly and with never-ceasing variety. The Baptist missionaries in Brazil took Blonnye to their hearts. The Cowserts and the Bratchers seemed to have a mysterious ability to anticipate his needs. They recommended the best teachers to him. They found him a place to live. They invited him to their homes again and again.

Within a few months after Blonnye arrived in Rio, Jack Cowsert began to involve Blonnye in his work. Despite his limited progress with Portuguese, he was able to pick up something of the burden of the overloaded missionaries.

And to think Dr. Ray had tried to keep him from coming by saying they had no pressing needs! Blonnye felt increasingly sure he had made the right decision. Yet, despite good offers of well-meaning friends and even missionaries, he was no closer to appointment in early 1930 than he was when he decided to come in the summer of 1929. In fact, with the stock market crash in the States and the deterioration of the total American financial structure, Blonnye was not sure appointment would ever come. For that matter, could he be sure his independent support would continue?

Sometimes when the day had not been too demanding, he would lie in his bed at night and take stock of things. The money was still coming; his needs were being met. He was able to teach English, thus making a large portion of his expenses; and his friends were still depositing money to his account in Clovis. The Lord God was meeting his needs.

Often in such moments of reverie a face would flit across his consciousness. The forbidden, unreachable, preposterous dream. But then God would meet those needs, too, and he would turn over and try to go to sleep.

Blonnye Foreman adapted to the idea of celebrating Christmas in midsummer and to his routine of teaching young Brazilians English and in turn studying Portuguese. His stomach took with ease to the black beans and rice that were such staples of Brazilian life. My New Mexico training, he explained. He developed a voracious appetite for the exotic fruits of his south-of-the-equator home.

This adjustment facilitated an early entrance to the world of Brazilian *"Crentes,"* as the Brazilian evangelical Christians were called. Under the tutelage of Missionary Jack Cowsert, he began working out from Rio on preaching missions. At first he worked with an interpreter or "Interrupter," as the missionaries said, and then in his own halting Portuguese. The fact he was not afraid to try out his imperfect linguistic skills, regardless of how it sounded, helped him no little bit, and soon he was not only understood, but persuasive.

He relished the weekend rides out from Rio on the wood-burning Brazilian trains. Throwing sparks and spouting black smoke, the trains plowed down narrow-gauged tracks laid through palm trees, coffee plantations, cane fields, and beside small rocky streams running through green mountains. The houses of mud and sticks that dotted the area soon became a part of his way of life.

On weekends they would preach before a small group of *"Crentes"* and then take a meal with their Brazilian host—often in the most primitive of circumstances, but almost always in the most gracious of atmospheres.

Now and then the trains would stop at small stations and little boys would swarm over the cars selling cakes, coffee, cooked bananas, and fruit. Always there was someone selling a cage of chirping canaries or parrakeets.

Blonnye found it easy to like the Brazilian people, and they in turn took to his easygoing manner and obvious willingness to share their lot.

Before he finished his first year in Brazil, Blonnye Foreman had the joy of seeing a Brazilian friend make a public profession of faith in Jesus Christ. This thrill helped undergird his determination to increase his proficiency in the language.

It was at the dinner table in the Jack Cowsert's home that Blonnye heard of an impending congress of Latin American missionaries to be held in Rio in the summer of 1930. Such Baptist notables as George W. Truett and Dr. J.H. Rushbrooke of the Baptist World Alliance were to be in attendance, along with Dr. T.B. Ray of the Baptist Foreign Mission Board.

Blonnye realized that Dr. Cowsert was hoping he could get Blonnye together with Ray.

"This would be a good chance for you to meet him personally and let him see how well you are getting along down here. I feel sure he will recommend your appointment just as soon as funds are available."

"I don't know," said Blonnye. "Funds have been available through the promise of individuals for over a year now and he hasn't made that recommendation."

"I know," Cowsert said, "but there's a big difference between somebody you are corresponding with and somebody you are talking to in person. I'm going to make sure you get together."

"I do want to be appointed by the Board," Blonnye replied. "And whether appointed or not, I will continue to work with our Southern Baptist missionaries. But I am reluctant to get my hopes up because of the discouragement I've received from him again and again, even though others have reassured me that the Board would be appointing me."

"But I want to see you able to give your full time to this work in years ahead without having to worry about where your support is coming from," Cowsert added.

"So would I," Blonnye smiled, "but I'll have to admit, God has met every need up until now, and the possibility of some support in one of the places of service you people have offered me undergirds my assurance that he will continue to do so."

"You'll not have any trouble finding a place of service," Cowsert assured him. "The publishing house, the school at Vitoria, or one of our 'colegios' could all use someone like you. Of course, I am hoping you will watch the orphanage and some of my work for me when I go on furlough."

Blonnye was more excited about this than he dared admit to Cowsert. It not only recognized his meager progress in the language and in understanding the culture of Brazil, but it would deeply involve him in the growing work of Southern Baptists in that country.

The Latin America Congress was going to celebrate the fiftieth anniversary of the arrival of the first Baptist missionaries in Brazil. A pair of hardy Texas pioneers, the Bagbys, had opened the work in Rio a half century before and they were to be present for the celebration.

And so were the Erik Nelsons. Blonnye longed to meet the rugged apostle of the Amazon. In his river launch, the *Buffalo,* he worked the mighty river from its headwaters in Peru to its delta on the Atlantic, preaching the gospel and establishing churches. He was already a legend.

When the Latin America Congress did begin with its influx of distinguished visitors, Jack Cowsert was on furlough and Blonnye was attempting to supervise his work—the evangelistic work in the federal district of Rio and the orphanage. He also inherited Cowsert's car during his furlough, and thus was commandeered as chauffeur for visiting dignitaries.

He drove the visitors all over Rio. Inevitably, he and Dr. Ray found themselves together. While Blonnye was not sure how he should act, the aggressive, effusive Board secretary took the initiative, assuring Foreman of his love and deepest respect.

Blonnye shared the incident in a letter to one of his closest supporters, N. B. Moon, his former seminary roommate, now a pastor in Texas. "There's not much telling when if ever I'll be appointed by the Foreign Mission Board. There are a few working toward that end, but Dr. Ray has consistently refused to recommend the matter. Of course, I am sure he has reasons for doing so. Mrs. Bottoms of Texarkana, Arkansas, wrote to him offering to support me if he would appoint me, but he refused to do so. That makes three times he has refused offered support. I suppose he thinks I have been campaigning for such, but actually I've tried to do just the opposite."

Following still another meeting with Ray he again wrote Moon. "He told me he had nothing but the utmost affection for me, and the Board did, too. And that they hoped to appoint me, but things are very dark for the Board right now and he would not like to hold up my expectations of appointment in the face of existing conditions."

He stopped for a moment, refilled his pen, then continued, "And I imagine that's about it."

He was disappointed and he knew it. It's nothing personal, he told himself for the umpteenth time.

Blonnye finished his letter in time to dress hurriedly for a dinner with twelve missionaries from North Brazil who had asked Blonnye to dine with them. When he arrived at the home where they were to eat, he was surprised to find Dr. Ray there also. He wondered if something was up that he did not know about.

After the meal it became clear. Led by Pioneer Missionary A.J. Terry, the North Brazil Mission formally extended Blonnye an invitation to go back into the interior in the state of Piau to a small village called Corrente to work in the Baptist industrial school and in the evangelistic work begun in that remote, primitive area.

Blonnye was thunderstruck. He had invitations from all over the area, but he had barely heard of Corrente. He knew it was considered to be the most remote and difficult field going. He knew the Terrys'

health made it impossible for them to stay with the school consistently. As Terry talked, Blonnye could see that Terry felt God had
sent Foreman to Brazil to replace him at Corrente. Foreman looked
at Ray. It was pretty obvious he knew about the invitation—it was
equally obvious that appointment did not go with it. . . .

3
April 10, 1955

(JAMES MUSGRAVE)

As the Musgrave family finished their dinner on a beautiful Easter Sunday, they decided they had every reason for gratitude. Church services had been unusually well attended and the message of hope seemed more meaningful than ever before.

Only the dark cloud of Blonnye Foreman's disappearance lurked over the otherwise serene horizon. Lingering over their small cups of dark coffee, a Brazilian custom they had readily taken to, they discussed once more what further actions they might take.

"Jan, surely we should have heard something by now. If Blonnye went to Corrente, I doubt if he would have stayed longer than this without letting the girls at Campos Belos know."

Jan nodded. "Yes, he would not want them to worry."

Musgrave thought of the girls Blonnye had been raising through the years. Most of them had come from the Corrente area where Blonnye had provided them a home and schooling. Most had been orphans. Several were already on their own and teaching school in some of the interior schools that Blonnye founded and nurtured with periodic visits in his small plane. With a wonderfully dedicated Brazilian nurse, Blonnye had raised a large family of orphans. More than once Musgrave had heard missionaries say with awe and respect that Blonnye's girls were as fine as anybody's children anywhere.

"He may be back in Campos Belos by now and we just haven't

heard." Jan had tried to comfort her husband several times during the week with the same words.

"That's true," Jim said, realizing vaguely they had been through the same dialogue nearly every day. "I feel sure I'll hear something when the plane from Arraias comes in tomorrow."

"If he's not back, what could possibly have happened to him, Jim?" his wife asked, obviously no more reassured by her hopeful words than her husband.

"I don't know." Musgrave looked up, his big hands spread in helplessness. "This is such a big country he could be anywhere—out of gas, grounded, even hurt." He stopped and rubbed his eyes with his thumb and forefinger. "That's what tears me up, Jan. If he's out there someplace hurt and I don't call for a search, I could be frittering away his chances."

"Yes," she said, "but the Brazilian Air Force won't take too kindly to an unconfirmed report. And what about the charges already pending against Blonnye?"

"I wish he would be more careful," Musgrave said. "Did I tell you what happened the last time he was here?"

"No, I don't remember your telling me."

"Well, I took him to the airport and watched him take off. Just after he took off another plane landed with three men in it. One walked over to me and said I ought to wait there because my friend would be back pretty soon and would need a ride back to town."

Musgrave paused to stir a lump of sugar into the cup his wife had just refilled.

"I asked the man what he meant, and he said Blonnye was flying into some of the worst weather he had ever seen. His plane had tried to get around it, go under, even over it. I took their advice and waited nearly an hour. Blonnye didn't come back. When I saw him over at Anapolis two weeks ago, I asked him about it."

"What did he say?"

"He said he knows that country like the back of his hand. All he had to do was get down near the ground and follow his nose. He's so confident he scares me." Musgrave looked up. "That reminds me of something I had forgotten."

"What's that?" Jan, clearing away the cups, stopped at the changed tone.

"When I saw him in Anapolis, he said he had just gotten his plane checked—an annual license or something. He said he had gotten by even though he had a broken compass."

"A broken compass!" she said. "Wouldn't it be dangerous to fly a plane like that?"

"It surely would. In fact, I am wondering if that is significant," Jim added.

"Surely he got it fixed," she said.

"I hope so, but he was so blamed offhanded about the matter. He said that all the rules and regulations were not really necessary out there."

"Did the authorities ever dismiss that other charge against him? You know, the one for flying at night."

"No, but they evidently plan to overlook it because it was a mercy flight. They realized it was quite an act of courage to bring that woman across the mountains at night. I think they have several other alleged violations they want to check out."

"Jim, if he didn't have a compass, how in the world would he ever fly to Corrente?"

"I don't know." Musgrave got up from the table and stretched. "Like he says, he knows the country like the back of his hand. I guess he could follow the Serra Dourados up to that small river that leads into Arraias, and he could probably make it from there pretty okay."

"Assuming the weather's all right," she added.

He looked at her. Before he could answer, their telephone rang, stopping the conversation. They listened as their Brazilian house girl answered the phone.

"*Hola.*"

"*Senhor Musgrave?*"

"Yes, one moment please."

Jim excused himself from the table and went to the phone.

"Yes, this is James Musgrave." He paused. Jan walked from the kitchen to see what the silence meant.

"Are you sure?" he asked.

"What's the matter, Jim?" she asked. "Is it Blonnye?"

"You say there were five people in the plane?"

"Dead. All of them."

"I will go down at once," Musgrave said.

Hanging the phone up, he looked at his wife. "It was Dias. He says Radio Goiania just reported a plane crash in which two Baptist missionaries were killed."

"Two missionaries!" she exclaimed. "Jim, could that be Blonnye and the young pastor he was to pick up in Arraias?"

"Surely not. He said five people were killed. Only two people could get in Blonnye's plane."

"But who else, Jim?"

"Let's get the car; maybe we can get more information at the radio station," he said.

A few moments later Jim Musgrave stood before the Radio Goiania representative who was rereading the news dispatch about the plane crash involving Baptist missionaries.

"Yes," he said, "the report specified Miss Mary Ruth Carney and Valdice Queiroz."

"Jim, I can't believe it!" Jan said.

"Neither can I," replied Jim. "Surely there must be some mistake. But then again, what possible chance would there be to confuse those names?" he said, squashing his own spasm of hope.

Jan Musgrave began to sob quietly. "Poor Mary Ruth. She's only twenty-eight years old. She hasn't been out here a full term yet."

Jim comforted his wife, "I know, Jan. Let's remember what day this is, however. We do not need to feel sorry for Mary Ruth or Valdice. They're with our Lord. They're with our risen Lord."

He stopped talking because his own throat was tightening and he could no longer trust his voice.

The Brazilian radio manager was distressed. "I will go see if we cannot find more details."

"Yes, thank you," Jim replied.

"Oh, Jim," Jan Musgrave said, "Mary Ruth's dead, Valdice, dead, Blonnye, missing. When will this awful time be over?"

"I don't know," her husband replied. "I don't know."

He had no words to comfort her or himself.

The radio manager returned. "I'm sorry, *Senhor* Musgrave, but there are no more details. Maybe tomorrow we will know more."

As they drove home, Musgrave said, "I'll have to catch a plane to northern Goias. That's the only hope of getting any details at all."

"All right. Maybe you can get some word on Blonnye. Maybe he was up in that area."

"I doubt it. Itacaja is up on the Tocantins, a long way from Corrente. Blonnye seldom works up in that area."

"I know," she said. "I guess I'm just grasping at straws." Softly Jan Musgrave began to cry again.

The next day Jim Musgrave caught a plane to Carolina in the far north of the state of Goias. Early that morning he had gotten a radio message to Rio through an amateur radioman. He had also asked the man to make inquiries about Blonnye Foreman with contacts he had in the northern part of Goias.

At Carolina, Jim learned the tragic story of the death of the attractive young missionary, Mary Ruth Carney. She, as personnel secretary for the Brazilian Home Mission Board, and a companion, Valdice, were making a survey trip along the Tocantins River. She was carrying money for payrolls and had visited several of the schools, encouraging the teachers and arranging for supplies. Extremely popular, the vibrant young lady had friends all over the area.

Mary Ruth and Valdice had contracted with a Brazilian pilot, who owned a Cessna 170, to fly them to one of the remote schools. The plane that had brought them to Itacaja from Carolina had to turn back with motor trouble. They had felt fortunate to find another available plane and pilot. She had been told the pilot was very good and the plane one of the finest.

For some reason the pilot had booked a fifth passenger, despite the fact the plane was only certified for four. The Brazilian pastor who reported to Musgrave sorrowfully told how they had watched the plane take off and begin to climb. Then they heard the motor miss. The pilot had turned back toward the field, as if to return for a landing. The motor became rougher. The pilot banked again. It was obvious he was going to miss the strip, and as he tried to turn again, the plane stalled and plummeted to the ground, exploding in a searing ball of flame. It was over an hour before they could approach the wreckage. Identification was extremely difficult, made possible only by a wisp of cloth, a small watch, and a pencil.

This had been on Saturday before the Sunday Musgrave received word of the crash. They had buried Mary Ruth and Valdice with a brief ceremony at Itacaja the same day as the crash. The Brazilian Home Mission Board secretary, Dr. David Gomes, had already gone to Itacaja. There was nothing Musgrave could do.

Again he was overwhelmed by a feeling of helplessness. The next morning, before catching his return plane to Goiania, he listened to the children sing at the school at Carolina where Mary Ruth had visited only a few days before:

> O think of the home over there,
> By the side of the river of light,
> Where the saints, all immortal and fair,
> Are robed in their garments of white.

Late that afternoon he got off the plane in Goiania. Word had come from Campos Belos. Blonnye Foreman had still not returned.

4
1930

(BLONNYE FOREMAN)

Barra was one of those interior towns that, despite its propitious location at the confluence of two major interior Brazilian rivers, seemed unable to muster any importance for itself. Indeed, if the great riverboats that churned up and down the Rio Sao Francisco had not stopped there with a periodic transfusion of people and supplies, the little town might have withered away into the rugged *sertao* or desert country that surrounded it.

Cidade de Barra, the jumping-off place for the central interior, boasted a population of itinerants every bit as large as the year-round inhabitants. A most interesting, if rugged, variety, Blonnye Foreman concluded as he sat at a small table in the rundown dining room at the boardinghouse where he was staying.

Even though he had been this way once before on the exploratory trip to Corrente to decide if he should accept the work at the industrial school, he still had the feeling he was slowly being carried through a dream into another world. Long days on the river launch, belching black smoke as it moved down the Rio Sao Francisco, had accentuated that feeling that he was being drawn out of a life he had known and pulled into another existence. Though at times the countryside reminded him of the rugged space of eastern New Mexico, usually it was unlike anything he had ever known.

Once again he looked over his surroundings with the idea of mak-

32

ing a few notes and writing some long overdue letters. It was then he noticed the sullen stare of the hollow-eyed waitress who served his coffee. She was looking at the door. A large woman with heavy makeup, provocatively, if somewhat shabbily dressed, stood hesitantly on the steps. She smiled at Blonnye with a crooked, nervous sort of smile. He smiled back, and then, embarrassed, returned to his paper and to his coffee. He had had very little experience with the world, but he was pretty sure of the kind of woman who was endeavoring to catch his eye.

More than one of her type had approached him on the river launch. Once after the passengers had been told that a famous river bandit might try to waylay them while they were crossing a large sandbar, one of these bold ladies had come and asked him for his protection. "Surely no gentleman would deny a lady his protection," she said. Blonnye had been embarrassed then, too, and had simply walked away. Later in the sweltering cabin where his hammock hung, he chided himself. This was the very kind of person to whom his Lord would have ministered. God had not called him to this country to minister only to respectable types.

On the other hand, he was painfully conscious of his bachelorhood and of the fundamental assumption almost all people in Brazil made about bachelors. It was going to be hard to live an exemplary life. He not only had the problem of resisting temptations constantly thrown at him, temptations that seemed to know just exactly when his loneliness was at its peak, but he had the problem of avoiding even the appearance of evil.

The rustling of a skirt and the scraping of a chair being pulled out from the table just next to him brought him back to his present environment.

He looked up and immediately regretted it.

"Bom-dia, senhor." The woman was seated very close to him.

He nodded and murmured a weak *"Bom-dia"* in return.

Again he looked at his notes. Nervously, he made an effort to write.

He needed to avoid what he instinctively knew was going to be a difficult situation.

For eight days he had been staying at Barra waiting for the river launch that would take him first up the Rio Grande and then the Rio Preto to a small village where he would disembark and begin the cruel overland trip to Corrente. In fact, the gruelling days from Rio to Barra would be a picnic compared to the trip across the baking interior of Bahia to Corrente. That was the part that would take endurance.

How courageous a man was he? The thought of the river launch being raided by the feared Bandito Lampeao, who for twenty years had terrorized the *sertao* along the Rio Sao Francisco, had given him an ill-defined anxiety. His hands would sweat profusely despite the hot dry winds blowing off the *sertao* as he watched the river hands struggle desperately to free the stranded boat. The heavy green growth along the river loomed even more foreboding than the dry reaches of the *sertao* just beyond because of what might be hiding there. The dragon head on the bow of the boat seemed to mock his efforts to pray.

"*Senhor,* would you buy a young lady a drink?"

Blonnye looked up. He had momentarily escaped his situation in his reveries, but the woman had not. She was very, very present.

Blonnye Foreman looked at her, noting the painted face, the mocking eyes, and the semifrozen smile that she undoubtedly meant to be provocative. He started to turn away and not answer her, but remembering the incident on the launch, he quieted the panic and said softly, "I'll not buy you a drink, but if you are hungry, I will ask the waitress to feed you."

The smile immediately disappeared and was replaced quickly by a snarl. She uttered something between her teeth which must have been translated close to "rude pig."

Haughtily turning away from Blonnye, she signaled the waitress and asked for something that Blonnye's still imperfect grasp of the language failed to comprehend.

Again he turned to the piece of paper on the table in front of him. He tried to concentrate on the fast-moving events that were carrying his life deeper and deeper into the interior and farther away from all that had been familiar to him.

Where had Christmas gone? Thank goodness, some thoughtful friends in Rio had made it possible for him to have the traditional food and fellowship that goes with Christmas. He had been able to give a few gifts and had received a few in turn. All in all it had not been bad, but he had still suffered from the nostalgia of log fires, family and friends, and earlier Christmases in New Mexico.

On the thirteenth of January, Blonnye had taken a train from Rio to Belo Horizonte, where he visited with the missionaries there, and then on to Pirapora, six hundred miles inland at the head of the navigable portion of the Rio Sao Francisco. The river itself wound northward from that point into the interior reaches of the state of Bahia before turning eastward to the coast.

A week on the river launch from Pirapora had brought him to Rio Sao Francisco. There he received word that the boat that was to take him up the Rio Grande and then on up the Rio Preto to the place where he was to be met by riders from Corrente was to be delayed. And now, this morning he found out that it would be at least two more weeks. What could he do in Barra for two weeks? Already the loneliness was eating at him.

The angry muttering of the woman sitting at the adjacent table reminded him that his stay in Barra was not going well. There were some reasons for gratitude, however.

Just before leaving Rio he had gotten word from his bank in Clovis that additional funds had been deposited to his account by several friends. The amount not only gave him enough to replenish that spent for outfitting for Corrente—clothes, shoes, books, extra glasses, dozens of things he had heard he would need that far in the interior, including medicines and tools—but had left him with the assurance of adequate funds for nearly one year. He gave thanks for

God's provision and for the faithfulness of friends whom he had not seen in over a year.

He realized also that the recent revolution, which could have caused a great deal of bloodshed and major setbacks to their work, had come and gone with remarkably little interruption of life. Undoubtedly, the new leader would be dictatorial in his approach, but he might bring stability also. Blonnye felt fortunate when he talked to missionaries in Belo Horizonte. They had been caught in a cross fire and had barely escaped bombs dropped in the area.

With these missionaries, Blonnye had explored the craters and trenches that Federalists had dug to stand off the Revolutionists. The scars of fierce though brief resistance were quite visible.

He tried to share a few of these experiences in his letter. As he dated it, he was reminded of his hope to be in Corrente by the middle of February.

Maybe God was trying to teach him patience. Or, maybe God had a purpose for his being in Barra. Surely God wanted him there for a reason. This was Brazil. God had called him to Brazil. There were people here who needed his witness. He had tracts and a few New Testaments. Why not distribute them?

The sound of a chair shuffling on the tile floor next to him made him realize that he may have been ignoring the very reason God had brought him to Barra. Chastened, he turned.

"Excuse me, *senhora,*" Blonnye said.

The woman did not turn, but lifted her chin haughtily—in silent rebuke.

"I'm very sorry I have been so rude to you," Blonnye continued. "Perhaps I should explain why I did not buy you a drink."

Despite her obvious inclination to play the hurt role a little longer, the woman turned. Gradually, the hardness of her features softened as Blonnye explained to her his purpose for being in Brazil and the faith that had brought him there. Within moments after he had begun, the woman was telling him her problems, her desire to live a

different kind of life, her deep hunger to know purity, faith, and assurance.

Blonnye took one of his Portuguese New Testaments from his
pocket and offered it to her. It was the first Bible she had ever held
in her hands. He pointed out several passages to her and patiently
witnessed to her of the love of Jesus Christ. He told her about Jesus
visiting with the woman of Samaria at the well, and, as he did, tears
began to run down her cheeks. When they parted, Blonnye was not
sure the woman had really accepted Christ, but he felt he had grasped
a God-given opportunity which he had almost ignored.

He slept soundly that night despite the heat, the lumpiness of the
bed, the mosquitos, and the revelries of some leather-clad vaqueros
whooping it up old-west style.

The next morning he was awakened by a Brazilian Baptist evangelist who was passing through the area and had heard Blonnye was
there. Before the morning was over, they decided to have a series
of services in a *"Crente"* home where the evangelist was staying.
Soon Blonnye was no longer fretting over his delay. God was still
guiding him and God had brought him to Barra for a purpose.

Three weeks later Blonnye disembarked at a small village that
was little more than a few mud huts on the bank of the Rio Preto.
The long-delayed boat had finally arrived in Barra, and Blonnye,
bidding farewell to his fellow evangelist and several newfound
friends, began the next leg of his trip to his new home.

The boat was a far cry from the rather nice river launch on which
he had steamed down the Sao Francisco, but his excitement over
his experiences in Barra and anticipation at finally reaching Corrente offset the discomfort.

As he disembarked, he was greeted by a missionary named Crouch
and two Brazilian helpers. They had three extra mules—one for him
to ride and two others to carry his outfit. Within an hour after Blonnye arrived, the group rode north out of Formosa toward Corrente.

Blonnye had purchased a pair of riding pants and knee boots. He wore a heavy, long-sleeved khaki shirt and a wide-brimmed hat. He knotted a kerchief around his neck to shield his already tanned neck from the brilliant rays of the sun.

The trail led up steep gullies and over high ridges. Every now and then the caravan stretched out in single file to pass through a dry river bed and once or twice around bottoms filled with stagnant water. Crouch indicated that the innocent-looking little holes of water harbored vicious schools of piranha, deadly fish that can clean the flesh from human or animal in a devastatingly brief time.

"Don't make the mistake of walking your burro through that," he cautioned Blonnye.

The first night they made camp at the edge of a clearing in a scrubby forest of short *sertao* trees where a farmer and his wife eked out a bare existence for themselves and an even dozen children. Despite the meagerness of their own provisions, they offered everything available to their visitors.

The members of the caravan cooked around a campfire in the farmer's yard and swung hammocks from the low, scrubby trees. One of the boys volunteered to stay up and keep the fire going because jaguars in the area had been rather bold lately and had taken a goat out of the same yard only a few nights before.

Blonnye was getting the hang of a hammock, but chills, vomiting, and diarrhea made it a rough night. Crouch seemed to think he had a touch of malaria, plus some kind of intestinal disorder. The next morning he was weak, but still game to press on. Breakfast did not stay with him very long, but after he lost it, he climbed back up on the burro and urged it after the others, winding their way through a well-worn trail between high sand dunes.

It was like going through an oven. Weak and sore, he was still fascinated with the dramatic nature of the desert. He knew he ought to share such sights with friends when he got a chance to write again.

Just before noon the caravan stopped under some surprisingly tall trees flanking a pool of greenish-blue water. In fact, the clear water, plus the trees looming so tall over everything else, made the place an idyllic setting. Crouch pointed out to Blonnye that the spot was a favored stopover for people moving back and forth between Corrente in the lower part of the state of Piaui and Formosa, the only river port in the northwestern section of Bahia.

Then Crouch added, "But despite the fact it is such a favorite stopping place, I have seen people here only one other time in all the years I have been traveling back and forth."

Blonnye could believe it. Unable to rest that afternoon because of his physical discomfort, he walked to the edge of the little grove and surveyed the back trail. They were in a fairly high area, and he could see a long way in the dry, clear air. Far back on the horizon he saw a small wisp of smoke. He decided that was probably Formosa. But surely they had come farther than that. As he looked around, he wondered how anything could survive in parts of this country. The green little agricultural island along the Corrente River, where the Baptists had located their industrial school and established their farm, was understandably well known in the area. Anything that was prosperous and fertile in the midst of all this had to be well known, he decided.

He thought again about a conversation with his host of the night before. The farmer told Blonnye how fervently he wanted to send two of his children to school in Corrente, but he had no money. Blonnye had urged him to send them anyway, saying he would try to help him find the money. Crouch had cautioned him against that kind of promise.

He said, "Blonnye, there's no place to stop once you start that, and the money gets mighty thin. The food gets thin, too."

Blonnye, noting the emaciated look of the children at the farmer's household, realized that the bare necessities of survival were a problem in the hard frontier country.

The second night he climbed into his hammock weary, but knowing he was going to be able to sleep. A supper of black beans and dried beef acted as if it might stay with him and there was no sign of a chill, thanks to the medicine Crouch had given him during the day.

He prayed for friends, starting with the more recent ones he had come to know on the caravan, those he had met on his boat trips, his friends at Barra, the woman at the restaurant, the missionaries at Belo Horizonte and Rio, his supporters and prayer partners at home, and for the first time in quite a while, the one who had haunted too many of his quiet moments. There was a little more detachment and he welcomed it with relief. As he moved deeper into his new world, the old one retreated to a safer distance. That was good, because sometimes the loneliness and homesickness that came with it seemed to drain energy greatly needed for his current task. He was sleeping soundly when the hobbled burros shuffled nervously at the cough of a jaguar not too far away.

Later, he forgot the lumps, chills, bounces, bruises, and discomfort of the trail in the warmth, hospitality, and excitement he felt upon reaching Corrente. The Terrys were gone and the Crouches were obviously grateful for the arrival of Blonnye Foreman. He knew they were counting on him to pick up a large teaching load at the school, as well as help Mr. Crouch with the administration and maintenance of the school and farm. The evangelistic needs up and down the river were endless.

Fine Brazilian teachers and local citizens took Blonnye to their hearts, an experience which he found profoundly moving. In some ways Corrente reminded him a bit of New Mexico. The heavy adobe walls of the houses constructed by the Terrys and the Crouches furthered the impression. But that type construction supplied a coolness in the most depressing heat. Tile floors and heavy hand-hewn beams across high rooms gave his new home a distinctive charm. Modern conveniences were missing, but everything built to replace them showed ingenuity and practicality.

Blonnye incessantly prowled the grounds to acquaint himself with his new world. He explored the rough sawmill and the adobe brick

austerity of the industrial school, the dusty town square with its hitch-
ing rails for the ever-present burros and the leather-clad cowboys.
He quickly got used to their fearsome dress and realized they were
as warm a people as he had ever met. They wore heavy handmade
boots with large spurs. They pulled leather chaps over leather pants
and, despite the heat, wore heavy leather jackets. Even their hats
were solid deerskin, round topped, with wide-stitched brims turned
up in front and back, and held on by a leather loop circling the back
of their heads.

The Corrente River vaqueros were generally bewhiskered, sometimes sporting a rifle, and always a leather-sheathed long knife or
machete. Most rode hardy little burros with raw leather saddles. Oc-
casionally one saw a jaunty cowboy on a short-legged horse.

Despite the coming and going of the vaqueros, Corrente was a
neat, orderly little town. Its people were proud and family-oriented.
There was a growing Baptist church and the industrial school was the
pride of the area. The Roman Catholics were not exactly excited to
have the Baptists in the area, but the people's enthusiasm for progress
and the opportunity the Baptists had brought more than offset any
hesitancy at that point.

The children at the school wanted an education more than anything else, and seldom presented disciplinary problems. When they
did, however, they were often extremely difficult. Soon after he began teaching, Blonnye, in frustration, drew a circle in the hot sun and
asked a seemingly incorrigible student to stand in the center of it. It
was a grueling punishment.

As Foreman stood in the shade and watched his student suffer, he
decided he was missing the point. He walked out to the student and
told him he would take his place and the student could stand in the
shade. Blonnye himself stood in the sunbaked circle until punishment
time was complete. His student seemed more chastised by the fact
Blonnye had taken his punishment than that it had been administered
in the first place. Tenderly, Foreman used the incident as an oppor-

tunity to explain to the young man how Christ had died in his stead. The student became a *"Crente"* and never forgot the incident.

A few weeks after Blonnye arrived, and after a particularly rewarding day at school, the students gathered after supper in his front yard and sang for him. He soon caught on to the words and added his own strong, attractive voice to the group. Thus they discovered their new teacher's talents and they encouraged him enthusiastically. Together, they sang for two hours. As he walked back to his room that night, he fell to his knees on the hard tiled floor beside his bed in weariness and gratitude. He thanked God for taking away the loneliness that had plagued so many of his days and nights in the early months, for health which had returned, and for the life he would try to give in service. When he crawled in bed, he was aware of a deep sense of well-being.

5
April 13, 1955

(JAMES MUSGRAVE)

Now, days after the crash, the plane no longer smoldered. The sun, however, had grown hotter and the meager shade offered by the scrubby sertao *tree that Blonnye Foreman had dragged himself under offered little shelter. Cold by night, thirsty by day, unable to walk or drag himself farther, gradually losing hope in searchers coming, Blonnye peered at the unrewarding horizon between swollen eyelids. . . .*

Jim Musgrave knew he was letting his imagination get away with him, and, yet, this vision increasingly haunted him—Blonnye, downed in his wrecked plane, unable to go for help, off from the beaten path (as almost every place in that area was). And he, Musgrave, the man most aware of his possible predicament, doing nothing about it.

Jim tried to drive from his mind the vivid imagery constructed by his own fears and to give himself to the formulation of some plans. The interruption in his search caused by Mary Ruth Carney's death had heightened his anxiety, and that anxiety seemed to inhibit his normally methodical and effective attention to detail.

Sitting at his desk, he traced the steps he had taken and the facts that had been gathered. Nothing added up. In frustration he wrote out the words, "It doesn't add up!" and broke the point of his pencil on an exclamation mark.

Musgrave slumped back in his chair and noticed again an issue of *The Commission,* the monthly magazine published by the Foreign Mission Board, which had arrived only a few days before. The magazine, usually two or three months getting to the missionaries, had been cruelly on time. It featured an article on Blonnye which seemed to mock Musgrave's inaction—"From Mule Back to Piper Cub." It had been done by Missionary Gene Wise. It outlined for the people at home the remarkable interior ministry Blonnye Foreman was having in his small plane.

Musgrave had read it very carefully to see if it would tell him anything more about his missing fellow missionary than he had been able to glean from other sources in his office. Most of it he already knew—Foreman's pioneering of the new work in the state of Goias by mule back; and then the remarkable acceleration of his work with the arrival of a Piper Cub. While the fifty-five-year-old missionary's flying had caused concern among his colleagues, as the article pointed out, it would have taken many years on mule back to do what he had already been able to accomplish in a few months with this small plane donated by Texas Baptist women.

Jim had noted in his research that Blonnye Foreman was soon due for a furlough. Blonnye had told him one day of plans to get some additional flight training while on furlough.

With a start, Musgrave realized he was being swept toward a morbid frame of mind. He could not let himself lose hope. After all, Blonnye had been able to survive a year and a half flying in the treacherous mountain and desert terrain and had always turned up safe and sound before.

But the vision of a downed, injured missionary persisted. Sighing deeply, Musgrave pushed back his chair, reached for his coat, and started out the door.

"Hey, where're you going?"

Jim Musgrave turned and looked at his wife. "I'm going down to the airport and meet the Cruzeiro do Sul plane from Arraias. There may be somebody on it from Campos Belos. Maybe they can tell me something. Hopefully, that Blonnye is back safe and sound."

A half hour later Jim Musgrave stood at the Goiania airport, towering above a half hundred people also waiting for the Cruzeiro do Sul flight from Arraias. The missionary caught sight of the DC-3 as it turned on final for the Goiania airport. *Please, Lord,* he prayed silently, *let someone have some word for me.*

He watched quietly, sharply aware of the contrast of the festive atmosphere around him and his own gloom. As the plane taxied to a halt and its props stopped turning, Musgrave spoke to a friend of his who worked for the airline. Then, he walked out toward the plane now disgorging its passengers.

"Excuse me. Do you know *Senhor* Foreman from Campos Belos?" He asked the question of each passenger.

The first two passengers shook their heads. The third smiled broadly, however, and Musgrave quickly took him aside.

"I have been trying to find out about *Senhor* Foreman."

"*Sim* (Yes)," said the man, "so have we; we are very worried at Campos Belos. We have not heard from him. His children are very worried also."

The word about children definitely disturbed Musgrave. The girls Blonnye had raised knew him well enough not to worry without real reason.

"When did you leave Campos Belos?" Musgrave asked.

"About four days ago," the man said. "I spent some time in Arraias before coming down here."

"Thank you so much, *senhor,*" Musgrave said. He ran after several other passengers to see if anybody else was from Campos Belos. He needed later information if he could possibly get it.

It was midafternoon when Musgrave pulled his car into the small driveway of his home in Goiania. The trip to the airport had turned up nothing new. Blonnye had still been missing four days ago. The only new word he had, and that was very intangible, was that the children themselves were worried.

Blonnye cared so much for those children that he would not do anything to worry them unduly . . . if he could help it. The thought pained Musgrave. It was not really fair to call them children. In fact, several of Blonnye's "children" were away studying. Musgrave tried to recall their whereabouts. Two in the training school in Rio and one in nursing? And of course there is the young preacher. Was he still in *colegio* or had he gone to seminary?

But now he was running from his responsibilities. He had to take some action. Should he go to the Brazilian Air Force? He had to decide—and he had to decide today. He could not stand living with the thought that Blonnye might be down some place perishing from injuries or exposure while he, Musgrave, simply worried over the possibilities. On the other hand, if nothing was wrong, pulling the Air Force into an air search would definitely cause problems for Blonnye. If nothing were wrong, Blonnye himself would not appreciate the difficulty such a search would cause him: the investigations, the red tape, the possibility he might lose his license. But how do you weigh that against his very life? Musgrave sat in his car wrestling with the alternatives.

"Jim?"

He looked up at his wife, who emerged from the house.

"A man just called and said he had heard you were seeking information about Blonnye. He said he received two letters from Campos Belos on the Cruzeiro do Sul plane. He . . ."

"Did they give any news?" Anxiously, Musgrave spoke before his wife had a chance to complete her report.

"Yes, but I am afraid it's not what we're looking for," she said. "They still have no word. They feel that something must be done."

"Well, that does it," Jim said. "I've got to report to the authorities that he is missing and urge them to do everything possible to locate him."

"I agree. You have no choice," his wife said. "If we've got to make a mistake, let's make it on this side."

Musgrave smiled. That was the affirmation he needed.

"You want to go?" he asked.

"No, I'll wait for the children to get home from school," she replied. "I'll be praying for you."

Musgrave drove hurriedly to the airport where the Brazilian Air Force kept an officer in charge of aviational matters in that area. On the way a wagon cart blocked the road. Musgrave honked impatiently. He was properly chastised when the harried farmer finally moved the reluctant burro and tipped his hat in a gracious apology.

Musgrave nurtured one remaining hope. If Blonnye had indeed gone to Corrente, as the mechanic reported, then he could have landed there with engine trouble and not been able to take off. It would take several days to get word to some place where a message could be relayed concerning his whereabouts and his needs. But, as he ticked off the days since Blonnye had last been seen, Musgrave realized that possibility was becoming increasingly improbable. Some word would have to turn up immediately. Corrente was not that remote. Blonnye had so many friends there from his years of service that he would certainly have been able to get word out by now.

Musgrave tried to imagine the rugged station several hundred miles to the north and east of him. He had never been there. For that matter, very few missionaries other than those stationed at Corrente had been there. But the plane! The plane stationed at Corrente could have gotten word out. Unless it were gone. Musgrave felt a deep weariness over the tension of such speculation.

As he pulled up before the Air Force office at Goiania airport, he stopped and sat very still. *Was he being an alarmist?* Once more he visualized a plane down on some mountainside and a weakening Foreman beside it, patiently waiting for somebody to do something. Well, he, Musgrave, was going to do something. He got out of the car determinedly. . . .

6
1934

(BLONNYE FOREMAN)

A large black buzzard common to the *sertao* of interior Brazil circled lazily over the town of Corrente. Every now and then it flapped its wings and moved from a thermal that had played out to another one of the invisible elevators that, though nothing else seemed to be stirring, his sensitive wings could feel. Blonnye Foreman, standing in the dust in front of his home, watched it, letting his thought soar with the bird. Now it has one, he thought.

The bird began to circle. Its wings were rigid. Gracefully banking, it kept tightening the circle, but now riding higher and higher. It flapped its wings once more, then reversed its bank, still moving higher.

"He's got it!" Blonnye exulted in the bird's triumph.

All right, you big black buzzard. You can see more territory from where you are right now than I can ride on my mule in two days. The thought of the mule caused him to turn and walk briskly back to the house.

"I'd better get Pasqual to go see after my mule." The words were said aloud to no one.

He wanted to get away early the next morning to visit some Christian friends at preaching points he had neglected too long. Now that school was out, he did not want to waste time catching up. The trip would take him about a week; he should be back the following Sunday night. *Just in time for the mail,* he thought ruefully as he began to pack his saddlebags.

The night before, after the Sunday services, he had gone over to the Crouches to check the mail which usually came in by trail from Formosa—that is, if the boat had been on time in Formosa. It was a regular ritual for the station to get together at the Crouches after the service to read the mail, share information, and enjoy a late snack.

Seated around the room in large, comfortable, homemade furniture that somehow did not quite fill up the heavy-walled, high-roofed, tile-floored living area, they first read their mail. Now and then someone quoted a bit to whomever would listen. Blonnye had had plenty of mail all right, but some of it had been disturbing.

Crouch had said, "Blonnye, with all these people congratulating you on being appointed as a missionary of the Foreign Mission Board, there must be something to it. Maybe you have already been appointed and official word has been delayed. Surely we will hear something soon from the Richmond office."

"I'd like to believe that." Blonnye smiled wanly. "But, I've received letters like these before. I've gotten them every month or so ever since I came out here five years ago."

He did not share with them the real problem inherent in these rumors. Working on the assumption that the Foreign Mission Board had picked up his salary and allowances, the several people and churches who had constituted his major support were no longer making deposits to his account. Even if the Board were to appoint him soon, the gap before his first check could be most difficult.

Blonnye did not worry about eating. He knew no one would let him go hungry. But, what about the children he was supporting in school? The Crouches had warned him about taking on such a heavy responsibility. He had ignored the warning because there was so much need.

Not that Blonnye blamed the people back in the States. He knew the depression was imposing tremendous hardships. Many of them did not have enough money for their own needs. Their faith was sorely tried to fulfil pledges of support to their churches and the causes at home.

"Blonnye, I believe you will have a letter by next Sunday," Mr. Crouch said optimistically. "By the time you get back from this trip, you will have word that you are under appointment."

"That would be good news," Blonnye said. He still declined to share his own inner reservations and concerns with the family he had come to love so much. They provided such warmth and comradeship to his life at Corrente. . . .

That night, in his room, he let himself dwell on another significant piece of news that had come in the evening's mail.

She was married! Evidently to a mighty fine man. He knew he should be happy for her. The thing that bothered him was that it made so many dreams, so many hours of thinking about her while sitting on that mule's back plowing through the brush seem so foolish.

And yet, he knew their age difference had made it a ridiculous dream in the first place. There was nothing there, nothing ever that would suggest the slightest possibility that they could ever have made anything of their relationship.

Blonnye decided that he was something of a near middle-aged fool. He had let the loneliness of the Brazilian nights, the ever-present temptation of a handsome people (often with no sense of moral restraint) drive him to dreams of someone who could take care of his loneliness. His thoughts resurrected some old memories, little vignettes that had special meaning and which he had so often called upon for solace. Now he would have to put them away, pack them in some old trunk of the mind. Shaking off the growing melancholy, he got up and began to shove some clean clothes in the saddlebags he would take on his trip the next morning.

Running down a mental check list, he carefully wrapped batches of medicines in pieces of waterproofed material. The possibility of rain was remote at this time of the year, but such remote possibilities had caused him difficulty before.

Life was a bit out of kilter, he decided. Sometimes everything was in place, in order. At such times he had no worries about family. There was money in the bank. His health was good. His dreams intact. Now things were beginning to fall askew. The money dwindled. The question of appointment was still up in the air. He was not really sure he felt good, but then perhaps that was the heat. And his dreams. Well, he was old enough to learn to face reality anyway. Still, things were a little bit out of joint.

By the time the sun was high the next day Blonnye was swaying easily on the back of his big $50 mule, seated in an old leather saddle made comfortable by many hours of riding. Fifty dollars was a lot to pay for a mule, but the mule was big enough for him to see over a brush that most people had to ride through. He had strapped his big machete to his saddle to hack away brush that had grown over the path. As he rode, it slapped gently against his leg. He let the mule set the pace as they moved down the trail. Twisting back in the saddle, he viewed the panorama of his back trail. His loneliness reminded him it was the first time he had made this trip without taking someone along.

Early in the afternoon he reached a small farmhouse where a family he had baptized a year before lived. To his delight, nearly two dozen of their neighbors had joined them. Some had come as far as twenty miles to meet the missionary.

After supper he sang for them until he was not sure he was going to have enough voice to preach. Then, he spoke to them about Jesus. Later, he gave away some Gospel portions, although only three of the group could read. Several indicated they wanted to believe, and he talked to them long into the night. Brazilians did not believe in baptizing immediately after confession of faith, so Blonnye asked his host to instruct the new believers until he could return a few weeks hence to see if they were ready for baptism. With satisfaction he realized they already had a church in fact, though not in organization, in the home. "The church in our house" was not confined to biblical times, he decided.

The next four days passed in much the same manner. He did spend two nights in one place because some of the Christians there had built a small place of worship and wanted to have at least two nights of services. Blonnye did more singing than preaching, but he reckoned it was just as effective. The interior people loved music and they could sing for hours.

By Friday sundown, however, he was not sure he was going to make his last preaching point. It was a rancher's he had been to on one other occasion, but he had come a different route. The rugged land he was moving through seemed to be unyielding either in opening a way for him to proceed at a normal pace or in giving him any signs of a trail he might follow. As dusk approached, he climbed off his mule and tried to coax his stiff limbs up a small scrubby tree. Possibly he could see smoke from a fire by this time. His friends would be cooking their evening supper out in the yard. The tree barely got him above the thick brush, however, and what he could see was disappointingly similar to what he had seen.

Climbing back down, he debated briefly as to whether he should gather firewood and set up a camp or move on. Then he decided to press on. He felt confident he would intercept the trail soon. But a half hour later, with heavy darkness enveloping the area, he was stymied by brush on every hand.

Reluctantly climbing off his mule, he unsheathed his big knife, and draping the reins across his left arm, he began to hack his way through the brush.

"O Lord," he intoned aloud, "thy servant could use thy watchcare in a very special way now. Thy servant knoweth that there are man-eating jaguars in this area and thy servant is sure that his Lord knoweth the whereabouts of these animals."

Blonnye Foreman was not sure whether he was serious or nervous, but it felt good and he kept on. "Thy servant beseecheth thee to turn them in other directions."

With a loud grunt he hacked a large limb in his path and pulled the stubborn mule, who probably figured he had already put in a fourteen-hour day, on through the narrow pathway.

"If it please thee, O Lord, thy servant would like for thee to convince any prospective mule- or man-eaters that this old mule is too tough to digest, and this thy servant is too run-down to be of any nourishment."

He stopped, realizing that his voice was getting louder and that he had arrived on a small knoll, topped by a scrubby tree. Few stars were blinking in the sky as there were some high clouds obscuring a large portion of it. There was no moon.

"Man," he said, talking aloud now, but to no one in particular, "it doesn't get as dark anywhere else as it gets in the interior of Brazil."

He stepped on a dry piece of brush and jumped involuntarily. Shaking a bit, he decided he would accept that as a sign that it was time to build a fire. Securing his mule, he chopped the brush into fire-size pieces and laid a fire just outside the circle of the little tree on the knoll.

Shortly, he had a comfortable blaze going, and though it had been a warm day, the coolness that settled on the *sertao* at night made the fire feel good. Too, he had gotten very hot and sweaty while chopping a path during the last hour, and the coolness of the night had begun to chill him. He decided to leave the saddle on the mule. Just why, he was not sure, but he did pull the saddlebags off and extract a few pieces of candy and a water bottle. That would be enough supper, he felt.

He convinced himself he did not really mind spending the night in the *sertao*. He had done it before, although come to think about it, this was the first time he had done it by himself. There was no place to sling the hammock, but he was not sure he wanted to sleep anyway. If Mr. Jaguar were about, the old gentleman might be hungry enough to zero in on him and his mule.

Sitting with his back against the scrubby tree, Blonnye stared into the fire for a while, then wrapped his arms around his knees and laid his forehead between his knees.

The fire crackled loudly and he looked up. Evidently he had dozed off, and from the looks of the fire, which was dangerously low, for at least a half hour. Reaching over to the pile of wood he had laid beside him, he threw three or four pieces on the fire and grunted with satisfaction as they immediately caught. The mule was shuffling about, looking at him quizzically, as if he were asking what in the world the missionary had in mind with this kind of accommodations for the night.

Now the fire burned brightly with very little noise, but there was noise outside the circle of light, and both Blonnye and the mule heard it. Was it something walking? There was so little breeze it couldn't be branches rubbing. They heard it again, then everything became quiet. Too quiet.

Once more the fire crackled, or was it something else? Blonnye jerked his head up and realized he had dozed once more. The fire was again very low. He reached for wood by his side, but there was none there. He took his old railroad watch from his pocket and squinted against the burning embers to see what time it was. Two o'clock. He ached all over and he was hungry, and cold, but he decided he had already risked too much. The moon had at last appeared over the horizon, and while it wasn't much of one, it gave him enough light to proceed. He secured his saddlebags, threw them across the mule's withers and climbed on. Even the mule seemed relieved to move along.

Blonnye Foreman gave the mule his head, reasoning that in the darkness the mule could find his way better than Blonnye could. He was soon proved right, and he had to dismount less and less to chop his way out of dead-end spots. Finally, the mule picked out a path that Blonnye would have sworn was a trail of sorts. It played out just about the time he thought he had found the road.

Dawn saw them climbing out of a deep gully and up on a rare

grassy spot. Just on the other side of the grassy rise was a small pool of water. At its site Blonnye dismounted, washed his face, built a fire, and made some coffee. As the sun came up, the air quickly warmed and he decided to bathe.

As he undressed, he found to his chagrin that he was covered with ticks. Slowly he began to pick the little blood suckers from his body. Twice he was sure he didn't get the head and decided he would doctor the spots later.

About midmorning he reached the trail and within another hour he arrived at his destination. He evidently had traveled in a wide circle and come in from the very opposite side. He had almost turned in the wrong direction when he hit the trail. Only a familiar landmark had caused him to turn in the direction opposite from his compass.

His rancher friend was aghast at Blonnye's story of the night.

"Just two nights ago a man-eating jaguar killed one of my cows in that area. The carcass is not a mile from here. No one around here will ride through there at night. You must have been protected by God."

"I am sure I was," Blonnye said smilingly. He did not mention the noise he had heard during the night. Had God heard his halfhearted prayer and turned that prowler of the night from him?

The next day as he started back to Corrente, savoring the joy of having instructed a half dozen new Christians and noting the growth of his friends in the Lord, he thought about the trip. God had taken care of him. He had guided him right through the jaguar territory.

"Ol' mule," he said aloud, "it's a good thing you're carrying a man who believes in prayer."

Painfully he scratched at the sores left by the ticks. Two had been red and ugly looking that morning. He may have been a little late with his medical applications. But why worry about things like that? A God who could bring him through the jaguar's country could take care of tick bites.

Thoroughly mellowed by the experience, he chastised himself

for his fears about money earlier in the week. Only a year before, when he had really just begun to assume responsibility for supporting several children, his funds had also dipped dangerously low. At the very point he was ready to admit he had been foolish in taking on such a heavy responsibility a large sum of money had come from Rio de Janeiro. A man he had met while he was there studying the language—an American businessman—had left Brazil to return to the United States. As he got ready to board his ship, he pressed the money into Jack Cowsert's hand and told him to send it to Blonnye, saying he wanted to help him in whatever he was doing. The money had come just as Blonnye's own was gone and the fees were due. He had wept in a prayer of gratitude when the money came.

Had he forgotten lessons like that already?

"Come on, mule." He gave the animal a good, hearty kick as they moved down the trail. Corrente was around the next bend. It was Sunday night and he was looking forward to reading the mail and enjoying refreshments at the Crouches' house.

Later as he was cleaning up in his room, he noticed that one of the tick bites was definitely infected. Helplessly he dabbed a little more medicine on it. He was going to have to pamper himself for a few days so his body would have the strength to throw off the infection.

"The jaguar couldn't get me, but a pinhead-sized tick could," he mused.

At the Crouches he was greeted by a smiling Crouch holding an official-looking letter with a Foreign Mission Board return address. Blonnye opened it and read: "At a meeting of the Foreign Mission Board on yesterday you were appointed a regular missionary of the Board. . . ."

It called for a celebration.

"How does it feel to be a missionary, Blonnye?" Mr. Crouch laughed.

"Well, I don't quite know," Blonnye smiled in return. "What have I been these past five years?"

"Why shame on you, Edward," Mrs. Crouch said. "Appointment doesn't make a missionary. God's call does."

"I know," Edward laughed, "but it seemed too good an opportunity to pass up."

They laughed together and gathered around the table as Mrs. Crouch cut through the white icing of a beautiful cake, the ingredients of which had been hoarded for just such an occasion.

As they munched the delicious pastry and chatted happily, Blonnye felt good. Things were falling back in place again. The trip had been a lonely one, and yet somehow had purged him of the basic loneliness he had been besieged by so often. It was gone, at least for a time. Soon the children would be back, school would begin, and the routine would be good for him.

He had come out by faith—faith that people he loved and with whom he covenanted would support him and take care of him. The fact they were doing it through the Board now made no basic difference in why he had come. God had called him to do this, and though he could not have foreseen exactly where it would lead, he knew unmistakably he had been led. The fruit of his ministry was scattered all over the *sertao* around Corrente.

Later, as he said good-night to his friends and went to his room, he knew everything was truly back in place. It had never really been out of place in God's mind, only in his.

7
April 15, 1955

(JAMES MUSGRAVE)

Lieutenant Joao Armindo of the Brazilian Air Force stood up as James Musgrave entered his office. The lieutenant was short, swarthy, and slender. His wide smile revealed a bright expanse of white teeth and the full extent of a long but well-trimmed mustache. He offered his hand to the tall, broad-shouldered missionary.

"Ah, *Senhor* Musgrave. I am glad to see you again."

Jim realized almost immediately that he had met the lieutenant before. Then he remembered the lieutenant was also a practicing dentist in Goiania. The inadequate base and small complement that made up the Air Force installation at Goiania probably allowed plenty of time for the young officer to practice his professional sideline.

"Thank you, Lieutenant, but I am afraid I have come to ask your help."

"Certainly, my friend. What can I do for you?"

Jim Musgrave sat down beside the lieutenant's desk at the latter's insistence, clasped his hands, and pursed his lips as he tried to decide just where to begin.

"It's *Senhor* Foreman," he said.

"Ah, yes, *Senhor* Foreman," said the lieutenant. "I have met him; in fact, I have some correspondence here on my desk related to his activities."

Musgrave figured that it must be the latest night-flying incident, but he decided not to pursue the matter.

"*Senhor* Foreman is missing, Lieutenant Armindo. I've checked out every possible place he might have gone to make sure he is not just delayed. I don't want to cause any trouble, but I am afraid to wait longer. He could be hurt and further delay might be fatal."

Jim Musgrave rubbed his eyes and out of the misery of the indecision he had borne for days added, "In fact, my waiting this long may have already been fatal."

The lieutenant's wide smile disappeared as Musgrave spoke. He reached into his desk and extracted a form.

"This is very serious, *Senhor* Musgrave. I will report it at once and we will make immediate inquiries. Hopefully, we can locate *Senhor* Foreman. Often in this part of the world, a missing airplane is a slightly damaged airplane down too far from communications."

"You don't know how hard I've been praying that that's exactly what this means," Musgrave sighed.

"Let's see, *Senhor* Foreman's given name is Blonnye, is it not?"

"Yes, Blonnye Holmes Foreman," Musgrave replied. "He was flying a PA-18. I believe it's called a Super Cub."

Pointing to a pile of papers on the right side of his desk, the lieutenant, with a twinkle in his eye, said, "Yes, I have a full description of his plane here." Then he became very businesslike. "Tell me when you first realized Foreman was missing and what you know of his activities just prior to his flight."

Musgrave took from a manila envelope he had brought with him a sheet of his own methodical notes. Step by step he outlined all that had transpired since he had first been informed that Blonnye was missing from his home base in Campos Belos. He included dates, times, and the persons involved. He detailed every word from any person who had any idea of the whereabouts of Blonnye Foreman. The whole recitation took nearly twenty minutes.

At the end of the time the lieutenant looked at him and said softly, "The territory involved, *Senhor* Musgrave, is some of the most remote and desolate we have. Communications in this area are very poor. However, I shall dispatch an inquiry to all radio stations throughout the state. Would you like to walk with me to the radio shack?"

"Yes," Musgrave said. "I'm relieved to be doing something. This has been a very trying time. I think you've heard about the death of our fellow missionary, Miss Carney, in the northern part of the state."

"Yes," the lieutenant said, obviously sympathetic. "That was a very tragic accident. It looked as if the pilot had illegally loaded his plane. I am very, very sorry. Let's hope your present concern will have a better outcome."

The two men walked out of the office into the bright Brazilian sun and across a dusty stretch of road to the radio shack.

Musgrave waited with the lieutenant as the inquiries were made and answers received. A little over two hours after they had begun, they had received enough replies to further their concern. The only fact they could establish without a doubt was that Blonnye Foreman had left Anapolis early the morning of March 29. No reliable word about him could be traced since that time.

"Corrente is a possibility," the lieutenant said, "but since you have another plane stationed there, I hardly see how we could have failed to get some information from there even if he had mechanical difficulty.

"I think I must take the next step, as serious as it is, and order our own planes to begin an air search," the lieutenant said.

Musgrave nodded. He knew it was an expensive and even hazardous step, but it was the only choice they had left. Late that evening orders were given that would dispatch Brazilian Air Force planes from two separate fields early the next morning.

On a large air map behind his desk the Air Force lieutenant traced the area the planes would search.

"We'll try to concentrate on the area between Anapolis, Formosa, and Campos Belos first. Then we will work the area north of Dianopolis, and in the meanwhile I will ask a plane from Barreiras to fly north to Corrente."

Musgrave thanked the lieutenant profusely for all he had done and just at dusk left the office to return home. In one sense the events of the day had heightened his anxiety. In another sense he was strangely relieved. At least he was doing something. The indecision, the waiting was over. Before he retired for bed, he fervently interceded with the Lord on behalf of the next day's air search.

Early the next day Musgrave made a long-postponed trip to an outlying church that was requesting his help. It was almost time for the evening meal when he returned to his home in Goiania. As he was getting out of his car, a Brazilian Air Force jeep drove up and Lieutenant Armindo hopped from the right seat, asked his driver to wait, and walked over to the waiting Musgrave.

"*Senhor* Musgrave, I am sorry to report to you that we have no word at all. Our planes checked all the fields where he could have possibly landed, and have also flown the air route very carefully. They have avoided the mountains, assuming *Senhor* Foreman would also. Too, the higher ones have been heavily clouded all day."

He paused, took off his hat, and wiped his brow. "To make things worse, a moment ago I heard from the plane I dispatched to Corrente. Only one other plane has been there in the past two weeks and that is your mission plane. They have absolutely no word about *Senhor* Foreman and they are extremely worried, just as you are."

"I am not sure I should send the planes out again tomorrow. I wonder if you would go over your notes with me once more. Is there any other trip he might have taken?"

"Nothing that I know of," Jim said, "but I'll be glad to go over my notes again."

The lieutenant signaled his driver who brought an aluminum map case.

"I have an air map we can consult."

"Please come in," Musgrave said.

They walked into the house and Jim introduced the lieutenant to Jan and the children, and then went into the dining room where they spread the map out on the table. Jan excused herself to prepare coffee and cakes for the two men intently studying the map.

The lieutenant pointed to Campos Belos set in a wide highland area in the central part of the state. He traced his finger south to Goiania where they were, and west of Goiania to Anapolis where Blonnye Foreman was last seen.

He said, "As you can see, the problem with this route is that there are many mountains. I assume he would have flown up the valley from Anapolis to the Tocantins River, and then east to Campos Belos."

"Yes," Musgrave answered, "that's the way he usually flew; but this time, as I mentioned to you, I heard he was going to Formosa to pick up a worker."

"Well, that would have sent him up this side of the Serra Gerais. My planes flew all along that side today and made stops at these two small fields."

He pointed to two round circles on the map which indicated small private fields where a plane in an emergency or difficulty might have landed. "They have neither heard from *Senhor* Foreman nor have they seen a plane cross through their area during the period," the lieutenant declared.

Mrs. Musgrave entered with coffee and refreshments and the two men retired to the living room.

"What kind of work does *Senhor* Foreman do? I know he is a missionary, but I am afraid I am not familiar with the kind of work a missionary does."

Musgrave could see that the lieutenant was sincere.

"Foreman is responsible for the missionary work in the northeastern field. In his plane, he works all the way west to the Tocantins River from Campos Belos. Some of his work is as far north as Porto Nacional. He has started several schools and works with churches in the area. Many ranchers throughout his area, nearly 32,000 square

miles, have built small landing strips so Blonnye can land. Sometimes he flies in and takes sick persons out for medical help. More
often, of course, he preaches, directs the work of the schools, dis-
tributes literature, and, well, anything that seems right."

"Yes, I have heard about the schools," the lieutenant said. "In fact,
the reason *Senhor* Foreman has not been reprimanded for violations
of our air regulations is because of his fine reputation as a friend of
the Brazilian people. Even this most recent night flight will probably
be overlooked because he was bringing a Brazilian woman to the
hospital."

Putting aside his coffee cup, the lieutenant said, "They tell me
the woman would have died otherwise."

"I heard that," Jim said. "Did you know that the woman has been
one of his bitterest persecutors in the small town where she's from?
She did not ask Blonnye for his help. He found out about her condi-
tion from someone else and offered to help her."

"That is the mark of a great man—when he helps someone who is
his enemy. I believe the church teaches that is greatness, does it
not?"

"Jesus did tell us to love our enemies," Musgrave said. "Foreman
seems to have the ability to love people whether they are for him or
against him."

"And what about orphans?" the lieutenant asked. "The young
sergeant at the radio shack said Foreman has adopted several Brazilian children for his own."

"That's right. When he was at Corrente, where he lived for
nearly nineteen years before coming into the state of Goias, he built
a home and hired a nurse and took in over a dozen Brazilian orphans.
He has raised them as his own. I believe they even call him 'Papa.'
Several are grown now, and some are teaching in one of his schools.
Several others plan to teach, and another one is a preacher."

The lieutenant sipped his coffee thoughtfully as Jim finished
speaking.

"It would be a great tragedy for Brazil to lose such a fine man,

Senhor Musgrave. I am going to send the plane out again tomorrow."

The lieutenant got up and took his hat. "Well, I must be going, *Senhor* Musgrave. You and your wife have been very gracious to me. I shall keep you informed of any developments."

The Musgraves walked the lieutenant to the gate. "You don't know how grateful we are for your personal interest in Blonnye," Jan said.

The lieutenant turned around and looked at her rather strangely. "I am not entirely sure myself why, *Senhora* Musgrave, but I assure you I am interested."

The lieutenant put on his hat and turned around again, "By the way, when did *Senhor* Foreman begin flying? Did he fly in the war?"

"No," Musgrave replied. "He's been a missionary in this country since 1929. I think he learned to fly on his last furlough—that is, his last return to the States. I believe it was about 1947." He looked at his wife for confirmation. She nodded.

"It's only been about the past two years that he's been flying seriously."

"And how old is he?" asked the lieutenant.

Eyebrows raised, Musgrave said, "He's fifty-five. We looked it up just yesterday."

"It is strange a man that age would begin flying. After all, it is not exactly the safest thing to do—especially in this country."

Musgrave said, "I'm not sure I know all the reasons, but ostensibly he learned for this work. He's been able to reach areas and see people it would have probably taken him years to get to on burro or horseback. That's the way he explored most of that territory."

"Very unusual," the lieutenant said, as much to himself as to the Musgraves. Putting on his hat, he climbed into the jeep and waved to the two missionaries as the driver pulled off.

Jan Musgrave looked at her husband, "I wonder why it is that, only when we are threatened with losing them, we get so curious about people and what really makes them tick."

"I don't know, Jan; I've been pondering that one myself. I wish I did know Blonnye better."

Watching the departing jeep, she said, "It's very strange, but I think the lieutenant feels the same way."

8
1941

(BLONNYE FOREMAN)

On December 7, 1941, the little group gathered at the Crouches after the Sunday evening service waited impatiently as Blonnye Foreman adjusted the static out of his shortwave receiver. Finally, he was able to pick up one of the news broadcasts that they were told had been going on all day.

Blonnye settled back from the set into a straight chair and sat very still as the implications of the news became clear. The United States was at war. As far as they were from home, they still felt deeply involved.

"That puts the finishing on my furlough next year," Blonnye said. "Not only would I run the risk of getting torpedoed at sea by German U-boats, but I'm not sure the Board will even allow me to return."

"I don't know about that," said Mr. Crouch. "Maddry has been very insistent on missionaries taking their furloughs when they come due, and your six years will be up this coming summer."

Blonnye struggled. He knew he needed a furlough. He had gone to the States in 1935 for his first furlough and returned to Corrente in September of 1936. In accordance with the policy, he was expected to return to the States every six years. He also knew the Crouches were hoping he would take their twelve-year-old son back to the

States with him since the youngster was ready for schooling he could no longer get in interior Brazil.

"What worries me is the plight of the missionaries in the Orient where all this is going on," Mrs. Crouch commented.

"If we can trust these broadcasts, and I see no reason why we can't, many of them will probably be prisoners of the Japanese before many days are out. The Japanese are on the move throughout the Orient."

"Did you hear all the talk among the young men about joining the army?"

"Brazil will also declare war against Germany and Japan," said Mr. Crouch. "I'm sure many of these boys will want to go. They've been feeling very strongly about German subs sinking ships in the South Atlantic."

"You know if I do go on furlough next year, I'm liable to get drafted," Blonnye said.

"Why, Blonnye, you're too old," laughed Mrs. Crouch.

"I'll just be forty-three, and being single with nobody dependent on me, I imagine they'll snap me up right away."

"Weren't you in the army once before?"

"Yes, I was in for three months. Right out of high school. A buddy and I joined up. We were sent to Albuquerque. They were training us in the big gym at the university there when the Armistice came and we were mustered out and sent home. We had just under three months of active service. That's all the army life I needed, however," Blonnye added.

"Why don't you become a chaplain if you have to go in the army?" asked Mr. Crouch. "You're a preacher, Blonnye, and you wouldn't be happy unless you had some opportunity to minister."

"Well, it's a long donkey ride to any of that," Blonnye added. "I guess I'll get some shut-eye. That ride out and back this morning left me pretty weary."

"Is that malaria bothering you?" Mrs. Crouch asked.

"No, I believe I've got it whipped. Whatever you've been giving me has done the job," Foreman replied.

"I imagine we're going to have trouble getting medicine in the months ahead," Mrs. Crouch observed, "and probably a lot of other things."

They all nodded.

"Before you go, Blonnye, let's gather around and pray about this thing."

The group held hands and Edward Crouch led them in prayer for a world in flame.

Six months later the Crouches helped Blonnye pack a caravan of mules and horses that would take him and young Edward to Formosa to catch the boat. They were to make their way to Rio and then try to catch a plane to the United States. The Foreign Mission Board had insisted that Blonnye take his furlough. This had greatly relieved the Crouches because they did not want to send their young son by himself. The Board also suggested that Blonnye take a plane since a missionary family had been lost at sea not too long before.

The packing completed, there were the tearful good-byes. Soon only thin columns of smoke revealed to the riders the location of Corrente as the caravan made its way down the trail toward Rio Preto, fifty miles away.

As he rode, Blonnye thought of how much things had changed— not only in the twelve years he had been at Corrente, but in the twenty-two years since the Baptist work had been started there.

A Brazilian family named Paranagua with twin sons, Benjamim and Joaquim, great landowners and cattlemen in the area, had brought Baptists to the area. Benjamim was a politician, becoming lieutenant governor of the state, and Joaquim was a physician. One day in the 1890's the physician was on a boat trip when he overheard a group of Brazilians plotting to throw Baptist Missionary Z. C. Taylor overboard to the man-eating piranhas. Joaquim intervened and he and Missionary Taylor became fast friends.

The missionary gave the doctor a Portuguese New Testament. He, in turn, sent it to his brother, Benjamim, who had opened a school in Corrente. Additional Bibles were purchased and sent, and as a result a small group was converted to the gospel.

In 1902, Blonnye had learned, Missionary E. A. Jackson made the tortuous trip to Corrente and preached to the group of believers. As a result, a Baptist church was founded. The Paranagua family furnished the leadership. It was seventeen years later, however, before Missionaries A. J. Terry and his wife moved to Corrente and established the school on a grant of land from the Paranagua family.

It was the Terrys who persuaded Blonnye to come to Corrente. They felt God had answered their prayers when Blonnye was making his decision on those railroad tracks at Clovis, New Mexico, at the same time the Terrys became convinced they could no longer stay on with the Crouches who had only recently joined them. With Blonnye, the Crouches had given the work a continuity of nearly twenty-three years.

Twisting back in his saddle to see if he could still see the telltale smoke fire of Corrente, Blonnye felt a deep sense of satisfaction. He had invested his life in a remote place, but the work was having a remarkable influence on many people.

"Come on, Uncle Blonnye, you're falling behind!" The excited voice of young Edward Crouch brought Blonnye back from his reverie. Spurring his mule lightly, he soon caught up with the group.

Two months later, Foreman and his charge were in the United States, safe and sound. After dropping young Edward off with relatives in Texas, Blonnye made his way home to Clovis and a joyful reunion with mother, sister, and brothers. His father had passed away during his first term of service.

It soon became apparent to Blonnye Foreman that the United

States Army, with an insatiable appetite for personnel, was still not ready to knock the doors down to draft a forty-three-year-old missionary. He resolved to let the events of his furlough year determine whether to try to enlist in the chaplaincy or to go back to Brazil.

Despite his residency in Brazil, Blonnye was as patriotic as the next man. The strong pioneering streak he had developed in the West made him especially eager to do whatever he could to help the war effort. On the other hand, a deep sense of personal involvement in the work at Corrente, the feeling of God's leadership, the knowledge that the Crouches were desperately shorthanded without him, faces and families, new Christians, and waiting preaching opportunities pulled him back.

Too, the children he was supporting held a tremendous emotional pull. The nurse he had hired to live with his "children" wrote him regularly of their development. Jamim and Angelica, the two oldest girls, were growing like weeds, Maria informed him, and the whole crew were getting fat as toads.

Despite everybody's preoccupation with the war, Blonnye found a warm reception among Christian groups and old friends as he told of his work. Telling them how the orphanage got started, one day he told a story that was almost too shocking to believe.

Blonnye was visiting down the river with one of his Brazilian friends one afternoon. It was a still, hot day, and as he rode up to a small hut built back from the river, there was a foreboding atmosphere.

Climbing down from his mule and tying it to a dead tree in the dusty front yard, Blonnye walked to the door and knocked. All he got for an answer was the wailing of a baby. Finally, he pushed the door in and found a pitiful child almost dead from malnutrition cowering near the shapeless form of her mother.

As Blonnye drew closer, he realized the woman was dead and had been for sometime. The stench was overpowering. When he pulled the child away from the woman, he had to brush from its wasted little frame maggots that had already invaded the woman's putrifying body.

Blonnye had held the tiny wailing baby girl next to his chest on the long ride back to Corrente. Taking her to the little house he called his orphanage, he and Maria, the nurse, had tried to get nourishment into the baby. It was days before they knew for sure she would live and many weeks before she would laugh.

One day as Blonnye carried her playfully around the yard, she smiled. After that, the smiles were more frequent, and soon life seemed to take on a different form for her.

Blonnye was not thought, even by his closest friends, to be an eloquent or a forceful speaker. But the kind of life he was leading and his obvious dedication mustered a powerful appeal, and so he was in great demand.

As Blonnye moved around from place to place during his furlough, speaking and renewing acquaintances, he became aware of a heartwarming fact. He was blessed with many unusually steadfast friends. His seminary roommate and confidant, N. B. Moon, not only had helped support him financially through the independent and depression days, but had continued to support him in special projects.

Ruby Atwood of Lubbock was a one-woman public relations and booking firm. It was all Blonnye could do to keep up with the opportunities she presented him. More than that was the kind of extra support she was constantly presenting him. She had given him an Electrolux kerosene refrigerator after his first furlough. Getting it into Corrente had caused no little trouble, but when it finally stood in Blonnye's adobe home, it was regarded as some kind of minor miracle. Hundreds of people had trooped into Blonnye's kitchen to see the strange box in which a fire at the bottom caused ice at the top.

Hearing Blonnye's stories of poverty and hunger throughout the Corrente area, Ruby and others organized to raise funds to supply meals to such children through the school. Blonnye enjoyed being with Ruby and found in her a never-flagging interest for all that he was trying to do and hoped to do.

The fall of 1942 was not encouraging, however, in terms of the war effort. While the tide had turned, the road looked long and the cost was getting higher.

In January of 1943, Blonnye enrolled for a semester of work at the University of Colorado in Boulder. He had taken a semester of work there on his first furlough to store up subjects in which he had teaching responsibilities at the institute. This time he wanted to study more math and take a special course in radio. Too, he needed to get away from the constant speaking engagements and to get some time for the reflection he needed to make a firm decision: to go back to Brazil, or to go into military service. He knew the pressure to go into the service had much to do with the war climate in the States. If he were back in Brazil, motivated by the stirring needs there, it might be another matter.

The mountain air was invigorating for Blonnye. He rented a small room near the campus and took his meals at a nearby cafe. His real break came, however, when one of his teachers let him use his mountain cabin which was in commuting distance. Blonnye spent several nights each week at the cabin, cooked his own breakfast, took a long walk in the invigorating pine, fir, and spruce forest, and drove down for his classes. Especially after the heavy snows, he made this his regular routine.

It was still nippy in early April when Blonnye awakened one morning in the rustic sleeping room of the little mountain haven. He jumped from under the cover quickly and hustled about the room, pulling on a pair of corduroy trousers, a shirt, and an old knit sweater. Then he went into the main room and lit a fire he had laid the night before. When he was sure it was going and had warmed his hands, he moved across the room to the efficiency kitchen and began to prepare breakfast.

As he set the table and began to pull the ingredients for his breakfast together, he realized how much of a nutritionist he had become: orange juice for Vitamin C, whole wheat bread, coffee without the sugar he probably could not have gotten anyway, and eggs plus a single piece of bacon he had been able to hoard (which he was not sure was good for him but which would at least taste good). He had developed a tremendous appetite which had brought him from a pretty skinny 140 pounds back to his "fighting weight," 160, filling out the hollow places in his six-foot frame. His dark hair once more had a good sheen to it, and he had color in his cheeks.

Shaving after breakfast, he noted the change. As he adjusted his glasses, he reckoned the decision to come to Boulder had been one of God's leadership. He needed the strength and energy that had come with the new routine. Many of his frustrations, he now realized, had been caused by fatigue.

That brought up another subject—the letter that had come the day before. During his second term he had made real peace with himself over his lonely status. What could not be could not be, and he had come to accept it. When his heart fluttered once or twice over a Brazilian girl early in 1941, he had come to feel he was really cured. Nothing had come of that, but it had taught him his heart was still there. It had survived the death of a dream. Now this letter.

He completed dressing and walked out to the small hand-hewn cedar table where the letter lay. He was not sure just what to do.

The letter confirmed a rumor he had heard upon his return. The one whose face had haunted him so many days and nights years ago had experienced marital tragedy. He was being asked to minister and offer counsel. Surely he was willing to do that. Could he do it without opening old wounds in his own heart? He would simply have to.

He picked up the letter, stuffed it in his pocket, and reached for his books. Making sure the cabin was straight, he started out for his car and the long drive to Boulder. . . .

Four months later he was on his way back to Brazil. The pull of Corrente, the school, preaching, his children at the orphanage, a work that called for a lifetime outweighed any service he might be able to give for the few months or few years in the army.

It was a circuitous route. First the Canal Zone, then Lima, Peru; then across the continent to Rio. There he stocked up on supplies, and especially medicines—which were becoming more available in Brazil, but which were a continued rarity in Corrente.

The war had made available some concentrated foodstuffs he was carrying back with him. Hunger killed as many as disease in the interior.

He took the train to Belo Horizonte and then to Pirapora. After a brief wait, he took the river launch down to Rio Sao Francisco. It hardly seemed possible that fourteen years had passed since he made the trip the first time.

A few days later, he arrived in Barra. It had not changed much except for the increasing number of friends he had there. The next day he was on a smaller boat churning up the Rio Grande and then the Rio Preto toward Formosa, and within a few days the familiar figures of Edward Crouch and several Corrente citizens welcomed him back home.

Soon he was caught up in the old routine—preaching, teaching, traveling by mule back and sometimes by jeep. The presence of motor vehicles in Corrente somehow lent a modern, more civilized atmosphere to the place. He was not sure he liked it, but since he had brought the first one in on his last furlough, he didn't complain. They had no roads to most of the places he went, so there were few times he could really enjoy it.

There had been a hard famine while he was gone, and there was a lot of sickness. He was quickly caught up in dispensing medicines and getting too many cures for his own good. Earlier a doctor, who had come to the area primarily at Blonnye's insistence, kidded him a great deal about the competition. Now the doctor was gone, seeking greener pastures, and Blonnye found himself treating malaria, syphilis, and many other common diseases.

Within months after Blonnye returned, the Crouches left for their furlough. This was a blow to Blonnye. First, he did not feel capable of carrying on the evangelistic work and the school. Secondly, he was lonely. He had many Brazilian friends, and of course his children at the orphanage took care of a large emotional need, but the absence of his friends left him wondering and unsettled. Too, his efforts to minister to the old dream had resulted in a renewed correspondence which accentuated his loneliness.

He wanted to do so much at the Institute and there seemed to be so little cooperation from the Mission. He knew money was short and personnel was short, but he had to have some help. He needed another couple in Corrente. He needed money to build a sawmill. Those people on the coast could decide to build a building and have it built. When he decided to build a building, he had first of all to make the materials to build it.

Taking his frustration out in strongly worded letters to the Mission, and pouring his heart out in long letters to friends, and eating his hours up trying to keep up with his responsibilities, he made it through the year.

In 1945 the Crouches came back on the heels of V-J Day. With the war over and desperately needed help and comradeship available, Blonnye's year of discontent was over.

9
April 16, 1955

(JAMES MUSGRAVE)

Jim Musgrave, leaning against the wall of the small Air Force office at Goiania, tried to benefit as much as possible from the narrow strip of shade offered by its roof. Shielding his eyes from the sun with his hand, he watched the lieutenant finish his conversation with the two returned pilots, turn, and walk back toward Musgrave. Jim had come up just as the planes touched down. They had flown out from Goiania that morning to search once more the area between Anapolis and Formosa.

"*Bom-dia, Senhor* Musgrave."

"*Bom-dia,* Lieutenant."

"I am afraid we still have nothing to report," the lieutenant said. "I have just talked to the pilots. They worked a fairly wide area between Anapolis and Formosa. It is a very rugged area around Formosa. If he is down in that area, he is going to be very hard to sight. But it is hot out here; come into the office."

Musgrave walked into a small office with the lieutenant. He was grateful for the officer's continued interest in the search. He had been desperately afraid that, after a few brief efforts, the lieutenant would write it off. After all, it was quite an expense.

"I have asked the pilots to make another run tomorrow morning. This time to the north." The lieutenant walked over to the air map behind his desk. "He could have gone north to pick up the Rio Das

Almas, especially if the weather was bad. His route might have followed the Rio Das Almas through this low country until it joined with the Tocantins. He would have then cut back toward Arraias. If he is down in that area, we may be able to sight him, because it is fairly wide open. One of the planes came down the river yesterday. But it was more or less a return home and not particularly a search mission."

Turning back to Musgrave, the lieutenant said, "Also I have gathered all the weather data on March 29. I think we can reconstruct what *Senhor* Foreman was up against when he took off from Anapolis early that morning."

Musgrave interrupted him. "Lieutenant, I want to tell you how grateful I am for your continued interest in Blonnye. I know it is taking your time and quite a bit of the government's money."

"Think nothing of it, my friend. I find myself more and more interested in finding *Senhor* Foreman and more and more prayerful that we find him alive. Working with you on this matter has given me a deep respect for your friend, and it has made me want to know more about him. No, think nothing of it; we shall continue to search."

Musgrave smiled appreciatively.

The lieutenant sat down and opened a sheaf of papers. One included a small hand-drawn map. "Come around here," he said to Musgrave.

Musgrave walked around the desk and looked on the hand-drawn map with a variety of symbols.

"Here, I have drawn in the weather systems that we were able to establish on the twenty-ninth. You will notice that it was clear in Anapolis. He could have taken off from Anapolis for Formosa and had clear weather most of the way."

"But it now seems he did not land at Formosa," Musgrave said. "Though the people at Anapolis told us that he was to have picked up a worker at Formosa and taken him to Campos Belos with him, we later found that Blonnye sent word to the worker to get to Arraias on the Cruzeiro plane so Blonnye could pick him up there. He did not land at Formosa, so that means he must be down somewhere between Anapolis and Formosa."

"That is what I thought too," said the lieutenant, "but if he sent the man on to Arraias and planned to meet him there, he could have flown directly north through the Rio Das Almas Valley between the mountains here."

Musgrave watched as the lieutenant traced the two long fingers of rugged mountains that extended north and south on parallel courses from their position.

"But all along here," the lieutenant added, "rain began to develop early on the morning of the twenty-ninth."

He drew a line across both mountains, roughly twenty-five miles north of Anapolis and running north and east about that much north of Formosa.

"Shortly after becoming airborne, *Senhor* Foreman must have seen the heavy clouds and rain developing across this line. His only course would have been to go up the valley. I do not believe he could have crossed the mountains north of Formosa."

Jim nodded; it was logical. If Blonnye were going directly to Campos Belos and there was any weather, that would be the course to take.

"But what about these mountains here around Lagolandia?" Musgrave said, putting his finger on a small mountainous area at the bottom of the valley between the two ranges.

"Yes, those are very rugged," the lieutenant said. "One of these peaks is 4,400 feet. It is my guess he should have flown well to the west of that area if he wanted to follow the Rio Das Almas. If he tried to go up this small valley over Lagolandia, he would have to go over high ground, and if the rain clouds had settled quite low, he would have no alternative but to penetrate them, or else turn around."

Musgrave sat down in a chair next to the lieutenant's desk. "What would he be up against flying into that kind of weather, lieutenant?"

"Well, that is very difficult weather to fly in, *Senhor* Musgrave. From what I can understand of your *Senhor* Foreman, he did not have an instrument license. He was a private pilot and probably was not trained to fly blind, as they say, or on instruments. If he penetrated an area where he could no longer see the horizon, then he could become disoriented, losing his sense of which way was up and down. It takes the average pilot without special training only about twenty seconds to lose complete control of the airplane."

"And you think he had to fly under that kind of weather?"

"Yes, he would have had to fly in that kind of weather if he wanted altitude enough to clear the mountains. If he were going to try to skim the ground along the river valley, he may have been able to avoid it except for brief moments. Then, perhaps, by relying on his compass, needle, and ball, he could have made his way through it."

The word "compass" struck a chill in Musgrave's heart. Blonnye's words concerning the inoperative compass came back to haunt him.

"Lieutenant, I hate to mention this, but I think I'd better. Blonnye was flying with an inoperative magnetic compass."

The lieutenant whistled softly. *"Senhor* Musgrave, unless your missionary friend knew that country like the back of his hand, there is no telling where he would have gone without a compass."

As Musgrave and the lieutenant silently contemplated the implications, their thoughts were interrupted by a knock on the door.

"Entre," the lieutenant said.

The door opened and a young sergeant Musgrave recognized as the radio operator walked in.

"We have received a message about the missing airplane," the young man said.

The lieutenant took the message and read it carefully. "It says here that your missionary friend passed through Dianopolis the twenty-ninth of March."

Musgrave got up and walked excitedly up to the map, ran his finger to the far north where Dianopolis would be. "It would be two-thirds of the way to Corrente.

"That may mean he is down somewhere between Dianopolis and Corrente. He got through the mountains!"

"Yes, if it's true, but I want to check it out."

Quickly he gave instructions to the operator, who saluted, turned, and left.

"Dianopolis," Jim said. "That would mean he had successfully penetrated that weather."

"Yes, that's what it would mean," the lieutenant said unsmilingly, "but, *Senhor* Musgrave, I find that hard to believe. Rain squalls were very heavy all through this area. The clouds were very low."

The lieutenant was quiet. He tapped his finger, rotated his chair, looked at his map, turned back, picked up his pencil, made a few notations, and rotated once again to look at the map.

"I am going to have the planes at Barreiras search the area between Dianopolis and Corrente once more. If Corrente were his destination, and if he did get to Dianopolis, then he must be down somewhere between. And if he did get to Dianopolis, that would solve another question."

"What's that?" queried Musgrave.

"Gasoline," the lieutenant said. "That Super Cub would have to land at either Campos Belos or Dianopolis for gas."

"Perhaps he did go up the Rio Das Almas to the Tocantins until he was out of the storm area and then he turned east toward Dianopolis," Musgrave offered.

"This weather might have included Dianopolis," the lieutenant said, "but that is a possibility."

"Would you be willing to drive with me to Anapolis?" the lieutenant asked Musgrave suddenly. "It is going to be some time before we get new information from the radio, and I want to talk to the people who last saw *Senhor* Foreman."

"I'd be glad to go with you. Let me call my wife and let her know."

On the way to Anapolis, the Air Force lieutenant and the missionary got to know one another better. Musgrave was pleased, but a bit perplexed, by the lieutenant's increasing interest in the man he was searching for.

"You know," he said to Musgrave, "sometimes I feel as if I am searching for an unreal person. All that I discover about him is so good that I think he must be some kind of angel."

"He is a very fine man," nodded Musgrave. "No missionary is an angel, but Blonnye is an unusually dedicated man. He's deeply committed to the pioneer work he has begun in central Goias."

"He picked a rugged territory to pioneer," said the lieutenant, "and I realize he is not all angel. He would not break so many of our regulations if he were an angel." The lieutenant smiled slyly at Musgrave, who simply grinned.

"Another thing I have wanted to know," commented the lieutenant, "though perhaps it is too personal."

"Not at all," said Musgrave. "I'll try to answer your question."

"Why did *Senhor* Foreman not marry? He is an attractive man. Did he have a tragic romantic life?"

Musgrave had pondered that one himself. He had heard rumors of a lifelong romance that had been on again and off again, and supposedly had been on again very recently.

"I'm not sure, *Senhor*. There are many women whom I know would like to have married *Senhor* Foreman. In fact, he has been quite sought after. I don't know much about his personal life, however. I do know he is committed to doing this work in Goias."

"It is a great thing," the lieutenant said, "to see a man with such a great purpose in life."

"I'm glad you recognize that, Lieutenant," Musgrave said, realizing that this was an opportunity to speak to his new friend. "Foreman's faith in Jesus Christ gives him this sense of purpose. It brought him here from the United States and it keeps bringing him back."

The lieutenant did not answer, but looked straight ahead, caught up in his own thoughts. Musgrave decided not to disturb him further.

The trip to Anapolis yielded nothing new on Blonnye's where-

abouts. The two men returned to the air force base further discouraged to find out they had nothing new from Dianopolis. They
parted, with the lieutenant promising Musgrave he would call him as
soon as the planes reported in the next day.

It was dark when Musgrave got out of his car in front of his home.
He listened to the night sounds and looked up at a clear blue sky
blanketed with bright stars. He wondered if Blonnye were looking at
those same stars, weak, and near death. *Would they get to him in time?*
He prayed to God they would.

10
1947

(BLONNYE FOREMAN)

Blonnye Foreman was frustrated. Not only was he beginning to wonder if the long trip from Corrente to Salvador, Bahia, had
been worthwhile in the first place, but now he was encountering an
unexpected delay in the little town of Juazeiro on the Rio Sao Francisco, where the railroad from Barra played out. The trip up the Rio
Sao Francisco from Juazeiro was easier than the one way down river
from Pirapora, and the boat was usually more nearly on time. Such
was not the case this time, however.

"*Uno, dos, tres, quartro, cinco!* Can't you Brazilians understand
simple Spanish?"

Blonnye Foreman forgot his own frustration as he looked at the
red-faced individual trying to make Portuguese-speaking Brazilians
understand very poorly spoken Spanish.

As he had expected when he first heard the voice, the man was an
American. Tall, slender, redheaded, but with a rugged ranginess
about him, the man would have stood out in any crowd. He was evidently trying to book a room at a boardinghouse already overtaxed
with people waiting for the delayed river boat.

"Pardon me, sir," Blonnye said, smiling broadly. "Can I be of any
help?"

The man immediately smiled in relief and said, "Thank God. An
American! Please help this servant of the people understand that I

do have baggage, but it's in my airplane, and I am too tired to go back and get it. I just want a room for me, not for my baggage."

Blonnye turned to the clerk and spelled out the man's problem. The clerk shrugged, smiled, and gave the man his room key.

Later as Blonnye walked down the street to a little restaurant to get a bite to eat, the same man caught up with him and insisted that Blonnye join him for dinner.

Blonnye soon discovered the man was a war veteran trying to find himself by seeing the world in a small plane. He had started out in the States months before, flying to wherever there was a place to land and staying until he felt the urge to move on. Blonnye was not sure from the young man's conversation just how he was financing this venture, but evidently money was not a major problem.

"I've got flying in my blood," the man said as he vigorously mixed rice and black beans with a heavy red pepper sauce that Blonnye knew would take a good stomach to tolerate. "I'd been flying fourteen years when the war began, and, of course, that was a flier's paradise."

He stopped to gulp down a large amount of the light beer he was drinking. Trying to cool the pepper sauce, Blonnye thought.

The pilot looked up, "You in the war?"

"No," Blonnye laughed. "I was a doughboy for three months in the first World War, but I didn't get in this one. I've been a missionary down here since 1929."

"Missionary? So, you're a missionary. I felt sure you were down here with one of the oil companies, or maybe making a killing ranching. Well, what a fellow does with his life is his own business, I guess."

Blonnye took it in good humor. "I guess it is. Are you trying to figure out what you're going to do with yours?"

The man looked up, not quite sure how to react to his question. He smiled, "Maybe I am, padre, maybe I am."

He paused and then took another healthy bite of the unholy combination on his plate. "My marriage broke up during the war. Not that I cared a lot. I was in hog heaven flying P-38's, but then when the war was over, nothing I tried seemed worth doing."

Blonnye listened. When the man seemed obviously unsure what to say next, Blonnye asked, "What kind of things did you try?"

"Oh, all the usual for a former pilot—crop dusting, feeder airlines, charter work. I even tried instructing for a while." He laughed and continued, "All that in about eighteen months. Then I bought a plane and decided I would go find myself. Since I had been all over Europe and part of Africa with the Air Force, and since I speak a little Spanish, I decided to come this way."

Finishing his food with a relish and polishing off the big glass of beer, he pushed back from the table and said, "By the way, padre, I like your Brazil." He smiled and added, "Even if they can't understand good American Spanish very well."

"Well, friend, you haven't seen Brazil until you've been out my way."

"Oh? Where's that?" the man asked.

Briefly, Blonnye described Corrente. He also described the tortuous way to get there, though he added that in all likelihood he'd be met by a jeep at the Rio Preto this time, since the road was fairly tolerable this time of year and since they now had several vehicles in Corrente. He resisted the temptation to talk about the good old days when everything was by mule and horseback.

"Any airfields out there?" the man inquired.

"Yes, there is," Blonnye replied. "We're getting some occasional air traffic now, so we've carved out a landing strip of sorts. We're even talking about getting a plane to ease our problem of supplies and communication."

"A capital idea," the man said. "Everybody ought to have a plane in an isolated situation like that."

Blonnye laughed. "Well, why don't you bring your plane and come fly for us?"

"Me? A missionary? No thank you, preacher; I've had all the religion I can stand for a lifetime. I had my fling at it, and to be frank with you, I've got more faith in my airplane."

Blonnye detected a deep bitterness in the man's voice. It was almost as if he protested too much. Blonnye wondered what kind of hurt or pain had caused such a deep reaction in the man.

As if the man sensed that Blonnye might be getting ready to probe deeper, he stood up and said, "Well, I've enjoyed it. Thanks for helping me out this afternoon. I believe I'd better get some shut-eye. I may be some place else tomorrow."

Blonnye stood, shook his hand, and watched him as he walked off. The man, Blonnye decided, was not too much younger than he. He walked back to his room a little sad, feeling he might have missed an opportunity to say something that could help the wandering aviator.

The next day his boat sailed, and with the pressure of his work, the incident was almost forgotten in a few weeks.

The little plane throttled back and glided out of the sun, lower and lower over the school grounds at Corrente. When it seemed it would not clear even the scrubby trees growing near the river, the pilot gunned the motor and skimmed swiftly over the station. Blonnye Foreman turned sharply as the plane darted overhead and watched it as it climbed for altitude.

"I can't figure out what else he wants unless it's to land," Blonnye said to little Elton Johnson, son of the missionary couple who had joined Blonnye Foreman after the medical retirement of the Crouches.

Turning to the boy, he said, "Come on; let's go to the airstrip and see who our visitor is."

Blonnye and the boy arrived at the airstrip in the jeep as the airplane descended over the trees at the end of the seldom used runway. The pilot gunned the engine just as the plane came to the runway and let it settle easily onto the dusty surface. It was skilfully done and drew an admiring whistle from the watching Foreman.

The glare of the sun on the windshield kept Blonnye from identifying the pilot, even as the plane taxied up to a few feet of where he and the boy waited. Only when the propeller stopped spinning and the small side door opened did he realize that it was the redheaded aviator he had met a few weeks before in Juazeiro.

Blonnye walked toward him, extending his hand. "Welcome to Corrente!"

"You said I would never be able to say I'd seen Brazil until I had been to Corrente," the pilot grinned, "so I really had no choice but to come."

Both of the men laughed. Then Blonnye introduced the pilot to the admiring youngster. Shaking hands with the youngster in a serious way that immediately captivated the boy, the American turned and looked over his surroundings.

"Friend, I don't know if you realize it, but you're sure a long way from anywhere else. I'd planned on arriving here with about an hour and a half's fuel to spare. As it is, I'm not sure I have a half hour's. I was right on the point of turning south to Barreiras when I saw the sun shining off the tin roof on the church downtown."

"Downtown?" Blonnye laughed.

"Well, I thought I'd give you the benefit of a doubt," the pilot grinned. Then turning serious he said to Blonnye, "Would you mind if I stayed around here a few days? I would really like to pick up the conversation we had at Juazeiro."

"Why of course! You're welcome. You can stay at my house."

"You're sure it won't be any trouble?" the man queried, though obviously relieved at Blonnye's hospitality.

"No trouble at all," said Blonnye. "I'm really glad to have you, and I think you'll enjoy getting to know the other missionaries here, and my Brazilian friends."

"Well, maybe I can even be of some help," the man said. "You know, fly in some supplies from Barreiras or something."

"You could be a big help," said Blonnye. "In fact, we've got a problem now of getting some mechanical parts for a sawmill I have just built, plus something for this rattletrap ol' jeep I'm going to take you back to the house in."

"Good." Again the man was relieved. Apparently, the fact that he could be helpful took the anxiety from his bold bid to capitalize on such a casual acquaintance.

As Blonnye drove the man to his house, he pointed out various buildings and almost ran over two cowboys herding three scrawny cows down the road. He wanted to be a good host. He was puzzled as to why the American had come to Corrente, but he was glad to have a visitor. Company was so rare an experience at Corrente he thought he could count on one hand every visit over a five-year period.

That night, after supper, the man began to talk. Blonnye came to understand the drive which had brought him to such remote environs.

"You may think I'm crazy, preacher, but my running around the world looking for something could be an effort to solve some serious religious doubts I have. I have tried to dismiss them; I've tried to drown them; but the fact is, I've either got to find a faith I can let my weight down on or I've got to make a full commitment to agnosticism."

Both of them were quiet for a moment and then the man continued, "I guess I figured if I came out here and watched people who have a faith that would bring them all the way to a place like this, I might find what I'm looking for."

Blonnye felt he ought to say something, but he wasn't quite sure yet just how to deal with the man. He felt if he started out too positively the man would back off.

"Tell me a little bit more about yourself," Blonnye said.

The man looked at Blonnye for a moment as if to determine whether the misssionary really wanted to hear him. Then, visibly relaxing, the man took a deep breath and began to talk. He talked long into the night. . . .

When Blonnye came in from the fields the next afternoon, his visitor, ready to pick up the conversation again, was puzzled by Blonnye's appearance. He was dressed in the homespun that the local farmers wore when they worked in the fields, and he was soaking wet and dirty from perspiration and dust.

"Preacher, I thought you were a teacher around here. You look like a farmhand."

"Well, we have a problem," said Blonnye. "I've been trying to pay some of our helpers for a day's work in the field, but I haven't quite known how to gauge what a man ought to get done during a day. I made up my mind I was going out there today and find out just what I could expect out of a man."

"But you're not used to this kind of work. You couldn't expect to do as much as one of those birds can do."

"But they don't start off with a healthy breakfast I had," Blonnye said laughingly. "At any rate, most of them outworked me, so I'm not sure I found out anything."

That night they continued their philosophizing, though Blonnye mostly listened.

At the end of two weeks Blonnye began to despair that he could help the man or the man would ever find what he was looking for.

"At times he gets so intent I think he's going out of his mind," Blonnye told Elton Johnson one day at school between classes. "Last night he came to me and said he was not sure he had ever met a real Christian. He said if he found out I wasn't what I said I was that would be it." Blonnye shook his head, distraught about the whole matter.

"I really don't know what to say next," he continued. "I'm human. I get tired. I get frustrated. I don't know what that guy expects of me and I don't know what else to say to him."

The pilot on the other hand did have more relaxed moments. Twice he flew to Barreiras to bring back needed supplies for the station at Corrente. Though the road was open now, it was a long and tortuous drive, and the pilot helped.

One night while having supper with the missionaries, he asked, "Why don't you people get a plane and a pilot out here? I've never been to a place more natural for this kind of service."

The missionaries began to talk about it seriously. A young Brazilian pilot who had just returned from service in the Brazilian Air Force, and who was a member of the Baptist church in Corrente, agreed to serve as their pilot if they could get an airplane.

Blonnye and his fellow missionaries queried the American pilot extensively about costs, weather problems, adequate landing strips, and upkeep.

"Why, you could learn to fly yourself," the man said to Blonnye, laughingly. "You could do in one day what it takes you a month to do on that flop-eared mule of yours."

Blonnye looked incredulous. "I'm forty-eight years old. You can't teach an old dog new tricks like that."

"Nonsense. I knew a man back in the States sixty-five years old who learned to fly after he retired. He's a good pilot, too."

That night as Blonnye and the American walked back to Blonnye's house from the Johnsons' where they had dined, the man was quiet. None of the rapid-fire challenges, the penetrating, pointed questions. Blonnye was puzzled, but he was too tired to push the matter.

The next morning Blonnye was awakened by the roar of the little plane sweeping low over the station. He ran outside, pulling his trousers over his pajamas as he hurried from his room. He got out from under the shade of the small trees in front of the house just as the pilot pulled up sharply into an extreme climb and made a 180° turn and leveled off just as it seemed he would lose air speed and drop out of the sky. Then the plane headed straight out toward the coast.

The man had gone as quickly and suddenly as he had come. Blonnye watched him go, shading his eyes against the rising morning sun. He had absolutely no idea whether the man had found his faith or lost it altogether. As he watched the little plane disappear over the horizon, he felt frustrated and spiritually impotent.

Earlier in the week one of their evening discussions had taken a strange turn. For some reason Blonnye began to talk about his own desires. The man pulled him out, and before he knew it, Blonnye was telling him about feelings he had scarcely shared with anyone else. He said he was winding up his career at Corrente. When he returned from his next furlough, he wanted to go some place else. He had marked out an area deeper in the interior in the state of Goias. He wanted to pioneer and begin a new work.

When he came back from furlough, he would be nearly fifty years of age, and yet he felt life would begin all over for him if he could start a new work. He stayed in good shape, he was used to the hardships and long lonely times of interior work. He knew from discussions with travelers that thousands of people lived in the remote villages of Goias and that they were very receptive to the gospel. He had been told of hundreds of children who desperately needed some kind of education.

Long into the night Blonnye had outlined his plan for beginning a new work and setting up small schools. "Some of my girls could teach out there," he had said. "Jamim will be able to teach very soon, and Angelica has already said she wants to go into mission work and start a school. I believe I could hire several others, too."

The pilot's earlier insistence that Blonnye should learn to fly had started his thinking to churning in that direction also. If he could learn to fly, and if the Board would buy him a small plane, he could work the interior in a way undreamed of by missionaries a few years before.

"Why, I could do in five years what it would take somebody twenty years to do otherwise," he said to the man.

Several days after the pilot had departed, Blonnye decided that whatever he had contributed to the man, the man had certainly contributed several key ideas to him. First, he and Johnson were committed to the idea of trying to get a plane for Corrente. The station desperately needed it and Blonnye was convinced that it was the thing to do.

Second, he decided that when he got home on furlough—coming now within a few months because the Board had again lowered the term of service, this time from six years to five years—he was going to learn to fly.

"If I can learn to fly and learn to play the pump organ," Blonnye said kiddingly to Mrs. Johnson one night, "I'll be all set to pioneer a new work."

It was more difficult for the Johnsons to kid about it, however.

"Blonnye, you're too old to learn to fly. Maybe you can learn to play the pump organ, but why don't you forget about this bush flying?"

Blonnye grinned and continued to nurture his plan.

In his room that night Blonnye reached behind the clothes in a drawer in his dresser to a small box he had secreted there. It contained the essence of another dream.

A few months before while on a preaching trip, a Brazilian had offered to sell Blonnye a small diamond. Despite his years in Brazil and the prevalence of precious stones there, Blonnye had little expertise for discerning the real thing from something only mediocre. Nevertheless, he had purchased the small diamond and later had a local goldsmith give it a solitaire mounting that turned out quite beautiful. The goldsmith had told him it was a good stone, worth perhaps $500 or $600. That had startled Blonnye and made him feel a bit guilty as he had paid only $25 for the stone. Of course, that was the price the man had set.

He wanted to show it to his colleagues, but if he did, he would also have to tell them why he had it—and that was one thing he did not feel free to share with anybody at this time.

Several letters during the last year had changed what had been a relationship of consolation to one of deep personal feeling again. Despite himself, he had felt smoldering coals of long-denied feelings begin to glow brightly once more. He was not sure what he could do about it. To do anything might be to jeopardize his missionary career.

Not to do anything was an option he found increasingly difficult to consider.

Slowly he fondled the ring and then replaced it in the box, slipped a rubber band around the box, wrapped it in a tissue, and put it once again in the back of the drawer. He walked to a small desk in his bedroom, took out a piece of paper, inserted it in his typewriter, and began to write. . . .

11
April 18, 1955

"Come in, Carlos." Jim Musgrave stepped back from the door as Carlos Fernandes, a close friend of Blonnye, stepped in.

"I am so worried about Blonnye," Carlos said. "Is there any word at all, *Senhor* Musgrave?"

Musgrave indicated a chair. "Please have a seat, my friend.

"No, I talked to the Air Force lieutenant a couple of hours ago and he said that the search planes had all reported in. They still have not sighted anything."

Carlos hung his head, obviously distressed. He and Foreman had known each other ever since the latter came to Goias. They had traveled together on preaching missions several times.

"What can you do now?"

Musgrave shrugged his shoulders and sat down, suddenly very weary.

"I wish I knew. I really wish I knew what to do. It seems there is nothing we can do until the Air Force comes up with something or somebody else gives us some information."

Carlos looked at the haggard missionary. "Tomorrow will be three weeks. I am beginning to lose hope. All the ways I have told myself he could still be safe seem to perish with the passage of time. All I am left with is the gnawing feeling that something terrible must have happened."

This so closely paralleled Musgrave's own feelings that he merely nodded, saying nothing. They both heard the telephone ring, and as he had done countless times during the past two weeks since he had heard of Blonnye's disappearance, Musgrave tensed involuntarily. He heard Jan go to the phone and answer it. There was a silence, and then she called out, "Jim, it's for you. It's the pastor from Anapolis."

Musgrave covered the distance to the phone in long strides and spoke almost sharply into it. Then he listened quietly. Jan stood by, trying to read his facial expressions. Carlos Fernandes walked up and did the same.

"And no one has checked it further?" inquired Musgrave. Again he was silent. Again Jan and Carlos searched his face as if somehow it would reflect what he was hearing.

"Thank you. I think we will drive up there."

He listened again.

"No, I think we'll come now, tonight.

"Yes, we'll come to your house."

Musgrave hung up the phone and turned to them. "The pastor from Anapolis says a rancher has come in and reported that a small plane has fallen on his ranch. He says the plane was yellow and two people were in it."

Jan looked at him, "But Blonnye's plane is green, and as far as we know he was the only one in it."

"I know," said Jim. "That's what we think. But we've got to check it out.

"Excuse me; I must call the lieutenant."

Quickly he dialed the number he had come to know by heart and waited quietly for someone to answer.

"Lieutenant? This is James Musgrave.

"Yes, I have heard something. The pastor from Anapolis just called me and said a man had come in from a ranch up in the Serra Dourada, saying a plane had crashed there. He said it was yellow and two people were in it."

There was a deep silence as Musgrave listened to the lieutenant's reply.

Then the missionary said, "I thought I would drive up there tonight."

Again a silence.

"Yes, I'd be glad to have you go with me. I'll pick you up at your office in about thirty minutes. Is that all right?"

"Right."

As Musgrave hung the phone up, Carlos Fernandes said, *"Senhor* Musgrave, would you mind if I went with you? I don't think I could sleep, knowing you were going up there."

Musgrave smiled, "Of course, Carlos, I would be glad to have you."

Musgrave went to his office and stuffed his briefcase with the files he had compiled on the matter. Jan pressed a vacuum bottle of coffee into his hand as he emerged and said, "Please drive carefully, Jim. Too much has happened."

Musgrave smiled reassuringly. He and Carlos climbed into Jim's Plymouth sedan.

The lieutenant was waiting for them at the base office. As soon as he was in, Jim wheeled the car around and headed for the road to Anapolis. All three men were quiet for the early part of the trip.

It was Musgrave who broke the silence. "Surely a man would not confuse the color green with the color yellow."

"I've been thinking that myself," said the lieutenant. "And from the information you have compiled, I do not see how Foreman could have had anyone with him."

"If there had been someone with him, would not their disappearance have come to light by now?" Carlos asked.

"I would certainly think so," said the lieutenant. "I feel sure this plane must be that of someone else. It must be from another area. Possibly it has been down such a short time that no one has reported it missing yet."

The lieutenant queried Musgrave further about the telephone call from Anapolis. "Did he tell you anything about the ranch? Where it was located? Did he say how long the plane had been there?"

"No, he didn't. He just said it was in the Serra Dourada, north of Lagolandia, and that a rancher had come in and reported it."

"I feel sure it will be checked out by the time we get to Anapolis," the lieutenant said.

The drive took a little over an hour. When they arrived at the pastor's house, the first question Jim asked him was, "Has anyone confirmed the story?"

"No," the pastor said. "The man who brought the report from Lagolandia is not the ranch owner, but he heard the rancher make the report and he came here."

"Is he with you?" asked Musgrave.

"Yes, he's in the house."

12
1952

(BLONNYE FOREMAN)

Blonnye Foreman had been out of the saddle too long. He readjusted his position again and again trying to catch the rhythm of the mule's easy stride. It was an unusually big mule for Brazil, and its long legs ate up ground quickly.

Blonnye was now in his third day on the trail since leaving his new home in Campos Belos for Parana, where he had the beginnings of a new school. Parana was located at the headwaters of one of the branches of the Tocantins. He had long hoped to get significant work started there. The sister of the woman who kept his orphanage had provided the opportunity when she offered to go there and begin a school. Blonnye was ashamed of himself for waiting so long to get there, take funds to her, and provide encouragement, but there was too much else to do. He was now supervising ten workers in central Goias. Eight of them he had brought from Corrente.

As he thought back to his first trip to Parana over two years ago, just after he had returned from furlough, he realized how long it had taken him to fulfil his promise to the people to give them a school.

There was not a cloud in the sky as Blonnye and his mule bore down the trail leading west to Parana. From time to time the mule would move down into a gully, then up the other side. Blonnye leaned back, his feet jammed forward in the stirrups as he went down, then leaned far forward with both hands on the leather saddle lip as the mule went up. Removing his broad-brimmed hat, he wiped a hand-kerchief across his perspiring brow, smoothing back his now thor-oughly sweat-soaked hair. As he did so, he glanced up to the sky and thought how quickly he could cover distances like this if he could ever get his plane.

Once more he was assailed by doubts about the fruition of his dream. He had taken his flying course in 1949 during his furlough year. That meant three years had elapsed now since he had flown an airplane. Three years of waiting, of red tape, of being delayed by the Board again and again; of having money preempted; of having fellow missionaries, meaning well, assured that Blonnye was not up to flying a plane, finding excuse after excuse to put off the matter. Three years during which he had ridden mule back all over the brushy highlands of Goias, pioneering a new work. He had be-gun immediately after his return from furlough.

At the thought of furlough, it was as if he had opened a door he struggled to keep shut most of the time. Painful memories came rush-ing up into the vacuum of the lonely ride:

Memories . . .

Hopes . . .

Dreams . . .

Romance . . .

Feeling like a young man . . .

Torn within by a great desire, a longing . . .

Fearful of all that was involved . . .

Knowing it could not be if he was going to continue his plan to re-turn to Brazil as a Southern Baptist missionary and begin a new work in Goias . . .

Emotions at first overwhelming the rational claims to duty . . . Then, realizing that his call, his commitment to return and begin a new work had priority over everything, even his deepest desire for love, companionship, his own family. . . .

In the late afternoon he stopped at a rare waterhole and let the mule drink. He wet the kerchief around his neck and wiped his face and the back of his neck, as well as the backs of his hands. The sun was setting into the west now, and he was going directly into it. He began to wonder if he would make Parana by dark.

The water hole was familiar. He had been there before. He remembered it as one of the places where he and his fellow workers had camped during the exploratory trip during early 1950.

He had come back to Brazil and finally secured permission from the mission and from the Brazilian Home Mission Board to begin work in the wilds of Goias. He had thrown himself into the quest with zeal born of a deep commitment on one hand, and the necessity to drown in worthwhile service his personal perplexities and disappointments on the other. The pain had not gone away easily. In fact, even now, two years later, he knew that he was not completely free of the sense of loneliness that had gripped him that painful year.

The survey trip, taking nearly three months, had provided the only solace he could have expected. The hunger of people for the gospel, the response of many to whom he preached, the desire of children for schools, and the zeal of parents to help him if he would but come and begin such work had been a great tonic.

He had urged several communities to build airstrips. To his surprise he found many more had already built them, trying to lure the government planes that were moving into the area to land at their little towns with supplies and communication with the outside world.

And then, at the end of the three months of grueling and exciting exploration, he had met Missionary Bob Fielden at Dianopolis, and they had retraced the whole three-month journey in Missionary Fielden's airplane in only four days. That four days convinced Blonnye beyond any shadow of a doubt, if there had been any left, that his learning to fly had been the right thing to do.

Even now, as he climbed back onto his mule and continued his journey toward Parana, he could remember the dryness of mouth that had come in those hectic days in Las Cruces, New Mexico, in 1949 when he had taken his flying lessons.

At fifty years of age his reflexes were not those of a younger man. While he had passed the physical examination easily, it had taken him longer than most to solo, and while he had given his instructor numerous moments of panic, he had finally acquired enough hours for his pilot's license. He was not sure he had captured the joy that some airmen talk about, the sheer exhilaration of being aloft, freed from the confines of earth's twisting trails, but he had enjoyed it.

Blonnye Foreman arrived in Parana just as dusk fell, and was greeted by the overjoyed little teacher he had sent there just two months before. Soon she was dragging him around by the hand, introducing him to friends of her work and parents of her pupils.

Blonnye had hoped she would be able to get twenty or thirty students together. She told him that she had fifty, and that twenty more were waiting to enrol in the next semester.

"Why, you can't teach seventy students," he said.

"Oh, but I must," she said, her face very serious. "I must. There is no one else to teach them."

Blonnye laughed, "All right. Hopefully, we can get you a helper next year."

"Oh, if you would do that, we could enrol a hundred!"

Blonnye shook his head, smiling, "I would like to have an evangelistic service here tomorrow night. Do you think the Alvarez family would mind my having it in front of their home again?"

"Oh, no," she answered, beaming, "they would be delighted. They are very fine Christians and many of their friends are interested in the gospel. Last week some people came here and tried to talk their children into leaving the school, threatening them and telling them I was a Protestant devil.

"Mr. Alvarez came and took up for me and told the children that the devil would not provide them with love and a chance to learn, that God would be the one to provide that kind of opportunity."

Blonnye listened to his excited worker for over an hour and found a great sense of gratitude in what she had been able to do.

Soon his weariness overtook him and he excused himself and piled wearily into his hammock to try to sleep off the rigors of the trail. The three days and two nights had left him bone tired.

The next day Blonnye met an American couple who had just moved to Parana. They were probably the only other Americans within several hundred miles. Blonnye was as eager as they to talk English with an American.

He found that the young couple were from California. They were sponsored by the New Tribes Mission, a small independent missionary group specializing in work with Indian tribes that had been forgotten by the march of civilization. They were studying an Indian dialect in Parana, hoping to go farther into the interior and begin their work early the next year.

Blonnye ended up taking a meal with them and telling them of his early days in Brazil. He enjoyed the role of being a senior missionary —twenty-three years in Brazil had earned him that title—and he was able to minister to some of their discouragement.

"When I went to Campos Belos just two years ago, there was only one Christian family there, a rancher and his wife. They are still two of my closest friends. It is because of them that I decided to move to Campos Belos in the first place. I built my home very near their ranch house. I began preaching at their home and soon we were invited to hold services in the homes of their friends.

"Things were very slow at first. The priest, upon hearing about my being there, caused a great deal of difficulty for me. But the school we started and the strong support of the local 'Crentes' soon won a foothold despite the opposition."

Blonnye stopped talking long enough to spear another slice of the juicy mango fruit that his hostess had prepared for him.

"Several indicated they were interested in trusting Christ, but they were afraid to make public their interest. Then near Christmas at the end of my first year there—it was as if God sent us a Christmas present. First, the mayor of the town trusted Christ as his Saviour. Then his father-in-law also trusted Christ. The next day the two sons of the postmaster made a public declaration, and the next night at a service a young man whose father was said to be the worst criminal in that section of Brazil came.

"Two young fellows to whom I had given medicine a few months before heard about the service and came the next night. And then the county sheriff came. By Christmas Day, where three weeks before there had been three 'Crentes,' there were now twenty-three. We organized a church at the beginning of the new year."

The couple warmed to Blonnye's story. They needed encouragement. They needed to hear someone tell them of days of frustration giving way to the kind of harvest which they very much hoped was on the other end of their frustration.

Toward the end of the evening, Blonnye's hostess took an opportunity to ask the question she evidently had been wanting to ask ever since the tanned, graying missionary had come to town.

"Do you have a family, Brother Foreman?"

"If you mean mother, father, brothers, and sisters, yes. My mother is still living and I have a number of brothers and sisters. My father passed away in the early years after I came to Brazil." Then he grinned, knowing that was not what she meant, "But if you mean wife and children, I don't have a wife, but I have sixteen children!"

At their puzzled looks he grinned again. "Shortly after I came to Brazil, I began work in a place called Corrente, up in the state of Piaui. Baptists have a small agricultural-industrial school there in an out-of-the-way area where I worked for nineteen years. During that time I established an orphanage of sorts and I consider those who grew up there my children."

They laughed with him as he, with typical father pride, told some of the stories of his children. Then, becoming more serious, he looked down at the empty coffee cup he was absently turning around in its saucer. "There was a woman, and I know I loved her very much, but somehow there was always something in the way. Now, this work seemed to have priority. So," he smiled, "I'm an old bachelor nursing a mule back and forth through the trails of central Goias. But I am happy in the Lord. I hope you'll be as happy as I am."

His new friends and the satisfaction he felt at the success his little teacher was experiencing in Parana made the visit most rewarding. By the time he was on the trail again, he was refreshed in more ways than one and ready for the grueling trip back.

The return trip did not go so smoothly. The first day was all right, except for the heat and a sore foot on the part of his mule. It threw the big animal's rhythm off. Blonnye found himself much the worse for it. When he made his fire and hung his hammock that night, he was sore and a bit sick.

The second night he found hospitality in a farmhouse where he was treated royally. The people expressed interest in the gospel, and when he departed for his final day's trip to Campos Belos, they made him promise to come back. Blonny told them it would take him fifteen minutes to reach them when he got his plane. The rancher indicated there was a strip very close by, and he would meet him if Blonnye would buzz the ranch house.

As he drew closer to Campos Belos, Blonnye had time to think about the days just ahead. Soon he would be leaving for Rio and a Mission meeting. There he would pick up the battle again to get his plane. He knew they had his request. Surely they would recommend that the Board appropriate the money to buy a plane. A friend in Memphis, Sam Johnson, had agreed to ferry the plane to Brazil at such a time as Blonnye could forward him the papers and work out the red tape.

Blonnye knew his fellow missionaries were only trying to do what they thought was best for him by delaying the matter, but he felt strongly they were limiting the progress of his work as a result. He knew he could do in one year with that plane what it would take him ten years to do on mule back.

Also, he felt sure he was going to have to battle for additional funds for his work. Because he had been hiring teachers without degrees or accreditation to work with him, the mission committee that supplied educational funds would not grant him money. He had tried to convince them he would never get any work started if he had to wait until he could find college graduates to come. Furthermore, the wages that such teachers demanded would greatly limit how much he could do. At first he used his own money. He brought in graduates of the industrial school and two of his adopted daughters.

On the back of his old mule, he calculated his bank account had shrunk to less than a third of what it was when he returned to Brazil for his fourth term of service. He did not regret that. He did not know what he would need money for anyway. The habit of saving every cent he could—since the early years when he had never known when the next dollar was going to come, or from where—was once more paying off. Most of that money had been given by friends for his work, and he really did not mind using it. Still it galled him that people far removed from the situation could make arbitrary rules that deprived hundreds of children of an education and hundreds of others of a chance to hear the gospel.

He kicked his mule firmly as it slowed before a steep section of the trail. He knew he was letting his feelings run away with him, but he had to make them understand the promise of his work. He had to find some additional support.

The mule topped a small hill, and Blonnye reined it to a halt. Ahead, nestled in a broad savanna area, was the little town of Campos Belos. The mule, realizing home was close by, started off at a rapid clip, and Blonnye relaxed in anticipation of a bath, clean clothes, and a big meal of beans and rice. He would top it off with a bowl of fruit and a glass of cold milk.

As if he had a congregation all about him, he began to sing "Higher Ground." The mule twitched his ears at the sound, but kept his pace.

The tune reminded Blonnye of services two weeks before in Dianopolis. If he possibly could, he needed to get there to baptize some new Christians before he went on to Rio. When he thought of the severe persecution he had met there only the year before and of the response that had come since then, he realized that God had been very good to him. His decision to come to Goias had been right.

How many lonely moments he had chastened himself with the thought he might have been wrong, that he had run ahead of the Lord! But now he knew he had made the right decision. This is what God had called him to do. This is what he was living for. Sitting tall and straight in his saddle, he sang some more. He felt good.

13
April 18, 1955
9:30 P.M.

(JAMES MUSGRAVE)

The pastor of the Anapolis Baptist church invited Jim Musgrave and the lieutenant into his home. Three Brazilian pilots, all friends of Foreman's, were also there when Musgrave and the lieutenant arrived. As the pastor introduced them, one said they wanted help. Two of them had flown their own planes three successive days at much personal expense, helping look for Blonnye.

"Then you have no more word than when I talked with you on the phone?" Musgrave was obviously disappointed.

"No, my brother, I am afraid that is all I know. A rancher came into Pirenopolis and reported that a yellow plane with two persons had crashed on his ranch near Lagolandia."

"Where is that?" Musgrave asked.

"It's just north of here," the lieutenant answered, and then turned to the pastor. "Lagolandia is a fairly level territory and has a federal official. I cannot understand a plane crash not being reported."

"The rancher's place is back up in the mountains. He calls his ranch 'Eulalia.' "

"How far?" the lieutenant asked.

"I do not know."

The lieutenant turned to Jim Musgrave. "It could be on the slopes of that 4,000-foot peak I pointed out on my map.

"I cannot understand why Foreman would have flown anywhere

107

near that. It is clearly marked on the maps." The lieutenant knitted his brow.

"Unless he was lost," Musgrave said.

"And in heavy weather," the lieutenant added.

"Pardon me, *Senhor,* but I flew my plane to Lagolandia." The first pilot, a man named Raphael, who had been introduced to Musgrave and the lieutenant as they entered the house, said, "Two days ago I flew as far as Lagolandia and then east of there and up the river. I thought he might try to fly up the river if the weather was bad."

The lieutenant nodded. He had said as much to Musgrave two days earlier.

"Could he have been trying to land somewhere around there?" Musgrave asked.

Raphael shook his head, "No, there's no landing field there, and very few places he could land in an emergency without washing out his airplane."

"*Senhor* Foreman was not a reckless pilot." The second pilot's name was Gomez. "I would not call him an expert pilot, but he was not reckless."

The lieutenant spoke up, "He may not have been reckless, but the record indicates he was prone to take chances from time to time."

"But only if he felt the cause justified," Raphael said fervently. "He has brought sick people to the hospital and flown medicines to people in isolated ranches and small towns."

"But he still took chances from time to time," the lieutenant insisted.

"Blonnye Foreman was very sure God was with him when he was flying," Raphael countered. "He told me many times that the most important thing about flying was prayer."

"That's right," Gomez said. "Blonnye Foreman always prayed before he flew his plane."

The lieutenant was evidently a bit discouraged at the direction the conversation was taking, so he changed it. "Are you sure they reported the plane yellow?"

"That's right," the pastor said. "The report said 'yellow.' I know, however, that *Senhor* Foreman's plane is green."

"Did you hear what kind of plane it was?" Musgrave asked.

"No, they only said it was a small yellow plane with one engine."

"And there were two people?" Musgrave queried.

"Two people is what they said," replied the pastor.

"If it is Blonnye, who could the second person be?" Fernandes asked. He had been very quiet most of the trip up from Goias, and other than acknowledging introductions, this was the first time he had spoken.

It was obvious to Musgrave that Fernandes was deeply shaken over Blonnye's disappearance.

Musgrave turned to the pastor, but the pastor only shrugged.

"Perhaps one of his workers," Raphael volunteered. "He was always taking preachers and teachers to the villages. And sometimes people would come to the airport and ask him for rides."

"That is right," Gomez said. "He often gives people rides."

"That is true, *Senhor* Musgrave," the pastor from Anapolis said. "The town is still talking about the time Brother Blonnye flew the Catholic priest back to Parana, when the priest had caused him so much difficulty and had raised so much opposition to his new school."

Jim Musgrave interrupted the fast-flowing conversation once more. "But it's nearly three weeks since Blonnye disappeared! Surely we would have had a report of a missing person!"

The lieutenant picked up the disturbing line of thought and carried it further. "Not if he were carrying somebody who lived back in the bush. Perhaps the people such a person would be traveling to see did not even know he was coming."

The pastor's wife entered with refreshments, and the seven men sat down to accept the hospitality of the home. Jim suggested to the lieutenant that perhaps if they drove on to Pirenopolis, they would find that the authorities there had already checked out the story. They might get some definite word.

"That is a very good idea, *Senhor* Musgrave. We can drive to Pirenopolis in a very short time, and, as you say, surely someone there has checked out the rancher's story."

After some discussion it was decided that Musgrave, Fernandes, the lieutenant, and the pastor would proceed to Pirenopolis. The three pilots agreed to stand by in case their planes were needed the next day for a search operation.

As they drove out of Anapolis toward Pirenopolis on a winding, dusty road, the lieutenant broke a brief silence by saying, "I was quite impressed with the dedication of the three aviators to *Senhor* Foreman."

"I was, too," Musgrave replied.

The pastor smiled. "Two of those men were won to the Lord by Blonnye's witness and they in turn won the third one."

"I appreciate their offer of help," Musgrave added. "Evidently they have already gone to quite a bit of personal expense helping out in the search."

"It is most unusual," the lieutenant commented.

Musgrave shot him a side glance and barely missed going off the road at a narrow curve.

"Whoa, my friend," laughed the lieutenant.

Musgrave smiled sheepishly, but gripped the wheel tightly with both hands. He had the feeling that before the night was out something was going to be resolved. Yet that was exactly what he did not want. The occupants of the plane were dead. Only if it were someone else would there still be hope.

"The man said a yellow plane," Musgrave spoke to no one in particular.

It was the lieutenant's time to glance at Musgrave. He said nothing.

The town of Pirenopolis was very small. Fortunately, the lieutenant had been there once before and knew where the justice of peace lived. While both Musgrave and the pastor had often been to the town, neither knew any of the officials.

Awakening the official turned out be a bad go. He was not at all impressed with a visit by an Air Force lieutenant, a "gringo," and a *"Protestante."* Nor was he impressed with their mission to try to find another "gringo."

He was very curt with them in answering their questions.

No, he had not checked out the rancher's story.

There would be plenty of time tomorrow or the next day. The people were dead; nothing could be done for them. Why did they not go back to Anapolis or Goiania and he would let them know as soon as the story was checked out?

It was all Musgrave could do to hold his temper, which was growing ever shorter with the long uncertainty and the possibility that the plane on the mountain was indeed Blonnye's.

It was the lieutenant who finally broke off the conversation. He did so with a few choice words to the justice of the peace about cooperation between the services and appreciation for people like *Senhor* Foreman who did so much for Brazilian people and who was, the lieutenant added, a better man than the justice of the peace or any of his forebears.

The justice of the peace, however, was not impressed and had a few prize comments of his own. Musgrave was impressed. He was impressed with the lieutenant's deepening involvement in the search for Blonnye Foreman. He wondered if there had come to be more than just a sense of duty in the lieutenant's help.

When the door closed in their faces, they turned and walked back to their car.

"We could return to Goiania and come back tomorrow," the lieutenant said. "We are going to be able to see very little tonight and I am not sure we can find the ranch."

"We can return to my house," the pastor said. "You can stay with us and that will save you from going all the way back to Goiania."

"If you don't mind, I would like to go on." Musgrave could not shake the feeling that had gripped him. He had to do something.

The pastor looked at the lieutenant and the lieutenant at Musgrave. "All right, *Senhor* Musgrave, we will go to the ranch."

It was after midnight when Jim Musgrave shifted the International into second gear to take a steep, rocky grade leading toward the Serra Dourada now visible in the moonlight. . . .

14
1953

(BLONNYE FOREMAN)

"*Senhor* Foreman! *Senhor* Foreman! Please, *Senhor* Foreman, we need your help."

Blonnye Foreman struggled out of a deep sleep at the sound of the insistent calling. Grasping the flashlight he kept by the side of his bed, he glanced at his watch. It was still only midnight, but, exhausted from a long muleback trip to a small ranch where he had baptized two new believers, he had been sleeping for nearly three hours.

"What is it?" he asked, cracking the door.

"*Senhor* Foreman, it is I. You must help us! My wife has a fallen jaw and only you can help her."

The man held a small flashlight up to his face as he talked, making sure Blonnye would be able to identify him, but all it served to do was give his face a kind of grotesque appearance. Blonnye recognized the voice as that of the father of a child he had helped nearly a year before. The man had come to him at night that time also.

The child had been very close to death with a high fever. He had already suffered several convulsions. Not sure he could do anything, Blonnye had told the parents he would give the child some medicine if they would not hold him responsible if the little boy died. He knew it could well be too late. The father insisted that Blonnye give the medicine to the child regardless of the risk.

113

"I'll take the responsibility," he had cried, pleading with Blonnye to give the medicine.

He had, and within hours the boy was free of fever, and within days up and walking around. But that had been a year ago.

"A fallen jaw?" Blonnye said, puzzled. "I don't know what to do about a fallen jaw."

"It is like this," the man said, slackening his lower jaw in a rather idiotic expression.

"Wait here," said Blonnye, "and I'll dress and see what I can find to do."

Returning to his room, he pulled on an overshirt and a pair of trousers. Sticking his feet into the sandals beside his bed, he walked over and lit a lamp hanging above his bedroom desk. Several books stood on top between a pair of quartz bookends. One was a medical guide. Taking it out, Blonnye bowed his head and asked for God's leadership. Then he turned to the index. He found the very subject he was looking for—the dislocation of a jaw. The text described just how such a thing could happen and what one must do to put the jaw back in place.

Grabbing a small bag of medicines, he hurried outside and followed the distraught man and one of his children to their house on the other side of Campos Belos.

He found the woman suffering terribly. Friends, trying to help her, had beaten and pulled on her jaw until she was bruised and faint.

"Please, Dr. Foreman," she said, slurring the words with her slack jaw, "help me."

Blonnye thought of telling her once more he was not a doctor, but decided that was useless.

Wrapping his thumbs in gauze, he took hold of her lower jaw and inserted his thumbs inside her mouth. Pushing down and backward as the medical book had described, he maintained a steady pressure until the jaw jumped into place. The husband, several neighbors, and the children looking on in awe from the edge of the lamplight uttered a great sigh and looked upon the missionary with great admiration.

Blonnye had a difficult time getting away. They tried to press upon him all manner of gifts as payment. Finally, he convinced them that all he wanted was to get back home and go to sleep.

The sky was clear and a bright moon lit his way as he walked back home. Now thoroughly awake, he felt glad to have been able to help the woman. He let his thoughts turn again to the excitement that had descended upon him two days before.

Word had finally come that his friend from Memphis, Tennessee, Sam Johnson, a pilot turned preacher, was flying a Piper Super Cub to him and was due in Belem around the first of July. Blonnye was to meet him there and accompany him down the coast to Rio where they would take care of the necessary entry procedures. The plane had been purchased for Blonnye by Texas Baptist women.

After four years of waiting he was to have the wings he so needed to nurture the work he had started throughout central Goias.

The excitement had been dulled by only two things. One was the fear that he had forgotten how to fly. The brief interlude during which he had taken flying lessons, soloed, and secured his private license seemed now rather unreal. That happened in the United States in 1949 and this was interior Brazil in 1953. Could he still fly?

The other concern that had tempered his enthusiasm was contained in a letter from the Foreign Mission Board, asking him to account for an overdraft in the mission account for teachers' salaries. Though the money had not been released, Blonnye had talked the treasurer of the mission into advancing the funds against Blonnye's conviction that the Home Mission Board of the Brazilian convention would refund the salaries of the teachers, but they had not been able to do it. Blonnye had exhausted his own funds and now the Board was suggesting he had misused funds.

The same letter inquiring about the matter included a question about Blonnye's plans for the care and upkeep of the airplane. Blonnye had assumed the Foreign Mission Board would provide this, but the letter sounded as if they expected him to do it.

He had written back as civil a letter as possible. In it he tried to describe the work that had been begun in Goias against great odds and the personal sacrifice it had taken. He shared with them the personal funds he had committed to the work and the lack of backing he had encountered on every hand from the Board, and even from some of his fellow missionaries. He had rewritten the letter and moderated it. It was not his nature to write sharp letters. Finally he had a courteous, but businesslike letter he thought would do the job.

Anyway, he was not going to let that worry him now. Tomorrow he would go with friends to Arraias. From there he could catch a plane to Barreiras, and from there to Recife, and then on to famous Belem at the mouth of the mighty Amazon. He should get there the day before Johnson was due to arrive.

He shook a little bit just as he arrived at his house. He was not sure whether it was from excitement in anticipation of the trip and the plane's arrival, or from a chill.

On the fifth of July Blonnye, thoroughly anxious after waiting nearly a week at Belem without any word from Johnson, saw a bright, shiny green plane turn on its final approach for the runway at Belem. There could be no doubt. That had to be Johnson.

Soon Blonnye was hugging the man like a long-lost acquaintance. Johnson in turn was full of the high adventure of having flown a Super Cub from the United States to Brazil. The two spent most of the evening talking, often at the same time, laughing, starting over, and doing it all over again before they finally got something to eat. It was midnight when they checked into their hotel rooms for a few hours of sleep.

Early the next morning the two men took off for the long flight around the long Brazilian coast to Rio. Stops at Recife and Salvador where missionary friends admired the new plane buoyed Blonnye's spirits. When they landed at Rio, he was positively elated. On each leg of the trip Johnson had turned the plane over to Blonnye and he had gradually reacquainted himself with the wonders of flight. He could still do it!

At Salvador he attempted his first take-off in the new plane.

"That's no take-off," Johnson said. "That's a departure."

"It was a little sloppy," Blonnye admitted.

He decided to postpone landings until he had a chance to practice some air work at Rio.

Almost as soon as they arrived in Rio, Johnson had to board an airliner to return to the United States. He was beginning seminary to prepare for the ministry and had allowed very little time for the odyssey to Brazil. A grateful Foreman saw him off and then turned expectantly to the task of clearing his plane through customs.

Four and a half months later he was still trying to clear the plane. Incredibly, the whole question had moved through masses of red tape in great wide circles accomplishing nothing. Blonnye, afraid to leave the situation, stayed on in Rio with friends. He stayed busy preaching revivals, visiting various churches in the area, and talking to potential workers for his interior field.

Blonnye had become close friends with Missionary Gene Wise, his wife, and their two daughters. Blonnye stayed in their home, and Wise, a former Air Force pilot, gave him a refresher course in flying after he secured limited use of his plane in the general vicinity of the Rio airport.

Blonnye had asked Missionary Aviator Bob Fielden to come down and accompany him to Goias on his first trip. He knew the navigational problems were well beyond his experience. Fielden, on the other hand, was unable to get away, and so Blonnye prevailed upon Gene to fly him in. Wise, caught up in Blonnye's impatient dream, was as eager as Blonnye to get him to his field. He had some trepidations about Blonnye's lack of proficiency with his plane and worked the older missionary hard to get him ready for the responsibility of handling the plane on his own in an interior setting.

On a bright day in December, Mrs. Wise prepared Blonnye and Gene a big breakfast and then drove them to the airport. They were both in high spirits.

Blonnye climbed into the front seat and Wise moved around to the propeller to crank the little plane.

"Switch off," he shouted.

"Switch off," Foreman replied, grinning.

"Contact," Wise yelled.

"Contact," Blonnye echoed, flipping the master switch on.

Raising his right leg high, Wise swung it back sharply and pulled the prop through. The 135-horsepower engine caught immediately, but from the way it caught, Wise knew something was wrong and he leaped clear of the whirling propeller.

Blonnye had left the throttle all the way open, and at full RPM the craft hurtled forward.

"Cut the throttle, Blonnye!" Wise screamed.

He knew Blonnye could not hear him over the noise of the engine. Wise grabbed a wing strut and tried to turn the plane from a hangar toward which it was moving with increasing speed.

Blonnye finally diagnosed the problem, chopped the throttle, and kicked a hard right rudder in time to turn the plane from the hangar, but not in time to keep the tip of his wing from hitting a parked plane a glancing blow.

The little plane then came to a halt and the propeller stopped, a sweating Foreman having finally closed the throttle and turned off the gas.

Wise, the quiet, patient sort, walked out to the plane, looked at the damage, and shook his head. Miraculously the other plane was not badly damaged, but Blonnye's new plane was going to need some repairs.

As Gene looked at the wing, Blonnye got out and walked around the plane to where his mentor and host stood.

"That thing just got away from me. I'm real sorry."

Wise looked at him and smiled, "Well, it could have been worse, Blonnye. We're going to have a slight delay, however, because we're going to have to get this thing fixed."

The damaged wing took an even two weeks to repair. When the plane was pronounced ready to go, Mrs. Wise took the two men to the airport once again. They loaded the plane and Blonnye climbed into the front seat.

Wise looked at him slyly. "Are you sure you're ready this time?"

Blonnye grinned and blushed. "I'm sure."

In a minute the little propeller was whirling steadily. Wise came around and climbed into the back seat of the tandem two-place plane.

Gene tried to teach Blonnye the value of a preflight check list. He had even suggested he paste one on the instrument panel, but Blonnye had not done it. After they had taxied to the end of the runway, Blonnye looked around and said, "You all ready?"

Gene said, "I am, but you're not."

"Whatta you mean?" asked Blonnye.

Gene silently indicated Blonnye's seat belt flapping on the outside of the door, slapping the bottom of the plane gently in the prop wash of the propeller. Sheepishly Blonnye opened the door, gathered in the errant belt, and secured it around himself.

He made a good take-off, however, and soon they were climbing in a gentle spiral toward the beautiful mountains that ringed the fabulous harbor at Rio. Blonnye, taking in the sights and thoroughly enjoying himself, began to fly a rather erratic course. Wise gently reminded him to hold the compass setting they had chartered for the first leg of the long flight to the interior.

The first leg of the flight was uneventful, but shortly after taking off for the second segment, a high deck of clouds began to get lower and lower. Blonnye dropped down to remain under them as long as possible, but finally he was flying at a level that would not clear the hills looming ahead.

Tapping Blonnye on the shoulder, Wise indicated he would take over. He had already assessed the situation and realized there was no alternative but to turn the plane around. They were not equipped for instrument flight; they had no navigational facilities to guide them through the kind of visibility they were looking at directly ahead. Shortly after he had reversed his course, however, he realized the clouds were settling all around. There was nothing to do but go up into them.

Calling on all the training the United States Air Force had given him and on the few instruments he could read over Blonnye's shoulder, Wise took the plane up through the cloud deck into the brilliant sunshine on top.

But now he had a problem. There was nothing except a magnetic compass to navigate by—no landmarks, no radio.

Foreman grinned over his shoulder enthusiastically, very sure Wise was going to be able to get them out of the sticky situation. Wise did, by flying out to sea, a trick he had learned in Europe. Sure enough, the clouds broke up over the water just as their gas became dangerously low. Gene was able to let down under and return to Rio five hours after they had left. Another false start.

That night the two discouraged men talked over their two abortive efforts to get Blonnye and his plane into the interior.

"Blonnye, we could have tried to push on through that stuff, but the chances are we would have ended up as a pile of junk on one of those hills between where we were and our destination."

"Well, I never was worried. I figured you knew what you were doing all the time." Blonnye had tremendous confidence in his younger mentor.

"Blonnye, just to be honest, I wasn't too sure. Going up through those clouds I was panicky several times and close to what they call vertigo. If we had not broken out into sunshine about the time we did, I'm not sure we would have gotten back here."

"You would have figured out a way," Blonnye said confidently.

"Blonnye, aviators have an old saying. I want you to remember it."

"What is it?" Blonnye asked.

"There are old pilots and there are bold pilots," Gene said. "What you must remember is there are no old bold pilots."

It took a few minutes for it to sink in. Then Blonnye grinned, "I think I get the idea, but I'm already an old pilot, so if I can just avoid being a bold pilot, I've got it made."

Gene shook his head and suggested they get some sleep before they tried it for the third time. "After all, the third time's a charm," he said.

Sure enough, the weather was good, and they were on their way, stopping from time to time for gas and noting the disappearing signs of civilization as they flew farther inland. On the third day they entered the state of Goias.

Blonnye felt satisfied with their navigation. "I took this course on mule back," he said laughingly as they plotted their last day's flight.

Blonnye soon zeroed in on the little village of Campos Belos and the small strip he had cleared near his home.

Gene had told Blonnye that he was going to have to learn to handle the plane all by himself, and so he offered no advice. He grunted once as Blonnye made a trial run about twenty feet over the runway to clear off assorted animals that seemed determined to camp on the strip. Then Blonnye banked, gained altitude, cut the throttle, lined up with the runway, and to Gene's obvious relief, made a perfect three-point landing.

When Blonnye flew Gene Wise to Barreiras to catch a plane back to Rio a week later, the older missionary was confident he could handle anything that came up with the little plane. He had practiced short field landings and take-offs and Gene had simulated a variety of emergency situations with him.

"Remember, Blonnye, your prime worry is going to be weather. When there is any question about the weather, just park your plane and get your mule out. Weather's the one thing you can't handle. In fact, with all the experience I've had, we were very lucky to get through that weather the other day."

"I'll remember," Blonnye assured him.

"Blonnye."

"Yes, Gene."

"Don't crash without me."

"I promise," Blonnye grinned.

After seeing Gene Wise off on the Cruzeiro do Sul DC-3, Blonnye climbed in his plane and was soon climbing steadily into the clear Brazilian sky on his way back to Campos Belos. His joy was unbounded.

The next two weeks he visited every strip in his area. He saw all his schools and many of his preaching points. Everywhere he went the people gathered in great numbers and rejoiced with him at the coming of his plane. The plane's identification letters, PTARM, came to mean "right arm" to Blonnye. The plane was his right arm.

A few months later as he leveled the plane off after climbing out from the small airport at Parana, he began to pray. Trimming the ship for hands-off flight—it had excellent stability—he prayed aloud. It was a habit he had gotten into in the plane. He laughed at himself once and decided he was trying to get God to hear him over the noise of the motor, but his prayers were sincere.

The plane was all he dreamed it would be. He was able to get to the far corners of his labor. The day before he had flown medicines to people where he knew it would make the difference between life and death. He delivered a new teacher to his newest school at Taguatinga. He had preached in the shadow of the plane's wing near a farmhouse where a Christian friend had gathered his neighbors. It was as if he could be everywhere at once. He wondered how he had ever been content with a ministry on mule back.

The sun was setting and the sky was beautiful. It was against the law to fly after dark, but he reckoned he'd be home just at dark.

A few minutes later he was straining against the faded light to line his plane up with the light-colored dust that constituted his now well-worn airstrip. Cutting the engine back, he listened with satisfaction to the whistling of the wind through the spars. With light back pressure he let the plane float in just over the edge of the runway and then let it settle gently to the ground. To Parana and back in one day! Who would ever have believed it?

15
April 19, 1955
3:00 A.M.

(JAMES MUSGRAVE)

Clutch. Brake. Gas. Shifting from second, back to first, then to second again, Jim Musgrave navigated the tortuous pair of trails ambitiously called a road. The Eulalia ranch could not be much farther ahead, and yet, at the speed they were making, he did not know when they would get there or, for that matter, if they would get there. They had come perilously close to getting stuck several times.

In the back seat, Fernandes and the pastor, both exhausted from the day of anxiety, were asleep. In the front seat next to Musgrave, Lieutenant Armindo stared ahead, his jaw set, lost in his own thoughts.

Musgrave broke a long silence. He wasn't sure whether he was talking to keep himself awake or to verbalize some of the feelings and memories swirling around in his head.

"About a year ago Blonnye and a young Brazilian pastor were visiting one of the places where Blonnye had started a small congregation. There was an old man there. I believe Blonnye said he was almost ninety years of age, and Blonnye had talked to him about trusting Jesus Christ. The old man was quite wealthy from raising cane in his fields, making the cane into whiskey in a small distillery, and selling the whiskey from a store beside his house.

One morning as he was getting ready to leave, Blonnye visited the old man and again urged him to trust his all to Christ. The old man, however, feeling that such a move would cause him to have to renounce his occupation, said he needed two more years to get his affairs in good shape, and then he would believe. Blonnye evidently tried everything he knew to persuade him before he had to leave. It was all to no avail.

"When he and the young pastor got to the field where the plane was tied down, Blonnye began the preflight preparations and noticed a slight faltering in his engine. After unsuccessfully trying everything he knew to correct it, he hired two mules and made the grueling trip to Arraias the old way. It took him seventeen hours. From there he caught a commercial flight to Goiania and secured a plane and mechanic to fly him back to his plane.

"When he got back to the town where the plane was, he left the mechanic with the plane and went back to see the old man."

Musgrave stopped his story and looked over at the lieutenant. He was gratified to see that the lieutenant was evidently interested.

"Before nightfall the old man decided to wait no longer, but to surrender everything he had to Christ. The pastor and local 'Crentes' were elated. By the time Blonnye got back to the field, the mechanic had fixed his engine. It was simply a matter of dirty spark plugs. Of course, the mechanic and plane to fly him out there cost Blonnye a pretty penny, but as he pointed out, it was a small price to see the old man come safely to Christ."

Musgrave chuckled a little bit at the recollection. "In fact, the way Blonnye interpreted it, the Lord fouled the spark plugs so he'd have to go back and witness to the old man once more."

"I have met that old man." The pastor's response from the back seat broke what had been almost a soliloquy for Musgrave.

"How is he doing now?"

"He is the cornerstone of the church there. He converted his store into a small grocery. He is raising corn in his fields instead of cane."

The lieutenant spoke up, "I'm afraid I don't understand you Baptists. Why was it important for him to quit raising cane and making whiskey? Does one become a Christian by not doing certain things?"

Musgrave looked at the lieutenant. "No, I didn't mean for it to sound that way, but we do feel that when a man gives his life to Jesus Christ, he will lay aside anything that does not honor Christ. Whiskey has wreaked such havoc among lives and homes that it is hard to see how making it available would be Christian."

The lieutenant did not reply. Musgrave pushed it further. "What Blonnye was asking the man to do was accept the fact that Christ had died that he might experience forgiveness and the promise of the resurrection."

Again the lieutenant was quiet, and with a silent prayer Musgrave gave his full attention again to keeping the International on the rocky trail.

"There!" the lieutenant said. "There, I see a light."

"Where?" Musgrave strained forward. "I don't see it."

"Drive forward a little more," the lieutenant said. "There. Do you see it now?"

"Yes, I see it, but how are we going to get over there?"

"Surely there is a turn-off a little farther. Let us go slow here."

In a moment the headlights revealed a sharp turn to the left. Where to turn off was not a problem because the road seemed to play out at that very point.

The pastor spoke from the back seat. "This must be it. According to the directions we got, there is no other ranch of any size in this area."

"I'm surprised there is a light this early," said Musgrave.

"You forget, my friend," said the lieutenant, "people get up early on ranches. It is now 4:00 A.M."

Soon Musgrave pulled the International to a halt before a cluster of adobe buildings. By Brazilian standards the rancher was fairly well-to-do. Only the loud barking of the two dogs broke the stillness of the early morning.

As the men disembarked from the International, a door in the main house opened and a man stood, framed in the light.

"Bom-dia, senhor," said Musgrave. "We need your help."

The rancher, in true Western spirit, was extremely gracious and invited them all in. He expressed concern about how tired they must be and offered to get them some food. A young helper was dispatched for that purpose even before Musgrave and the lieutenant were able to tell the rancher their purpose in coming.

"Senhor," Musgrave said, "we were told in Pirenopolis that a small plane has fallen here. We have come to see if it possibly was a friend of ours, a missionary."

"Ah, yes," replied the rancher. "It is true. A small plane has crashed on my ranch, though I was not here when it happened."

The rancher began to tuck his nightshirt into the waist of his trousers as he talked. "I was in town for supplies, but my workers tell me that a plane flew over the house once and then turned around and flew over it again. When he flew over a second time, they watched it until it disappeared. There were low clouds and rain showers and they could only see it for a little while.

"A few minutes later they heard it again, followed by a loud crash, and they saw a flash of flame up on the mountain. They went to it, but they would not go close. They are not very well-educated men. They are very superstitious."

The rancher ran both hands through his tousled hair and said, "As soon as I returned, they told me about it, and I walked to the site. The plane was terribly destroyed and the airman was inside, dead."

Musgrave stopped him. "There was only one person?"

"Sim, senhor, only one person," the rancher said.

Musgrave looked at the lieutenant and said, "We were told there were two persons in it."

"No, only one person."

"And it was a yellow plane?" Musgrave queried.

The rancher scratched his head. "I think it was a yellow plane or maybe green, possibly it was yellow and green. I am not sure about that, *senhor.* I am very sorry."

Musgrave felt a slow sickness creep over him. The other three men were very silent.

"Did you find anything in the plane to identify the man?" Musgrave asked, almost afraid his question would elicit information he could not stand to hear.

"Sim." The rancher turned and walked to a small cabinet. It was in the shadows of the room which was lit only by a kerosene lantern where they stood.

As the men watched, the rancher stooped down and removed a heavy metal box from the cabinet. Musgrave recognized it immediately as a battery box. He knew one would have been in the airplane because he had helped Blonnye pull his battery from the plane one time to exchange it for a new one.

The man walked over to the table where the lantern was and carefully upended the box. "I am afraid this is all that was worth bringing down from the plane," he said apologetically.

The three men watched as the contents spilled out on the table. There were several half-burned documents, a small card—evidently an identification card—some small wrenches, and a wristwatch. For a moment no one moved, and then, slowly and deliberately, Musgrave walked to the table and picked up the identification card. He held it close to the light so he could read it clearly. . . .

16
1955

(BLONNYE FOREMAN)

So much was happening. There was so much to do, and yet Blonnye had to admit that the busier he was, the happier he was. He thrived on the responsibility—the deadlines, the pressing of one engagement into another, the supervision of workers, the joy of baptisms, the greeting of friends. This was now the stuff of life for him. He was the Lord's man, and he was given up to this task. His own disappointments in life, the lonely nostalgic moments that intruded now less and less, the frustrations related to securing support for his workers—all faded before the sheer exhilaration of so much happening.

He prayed aloud a lot. "Sure beats talking to yourself," he told a friend. God, his Co-pilot. God, his Protector. God, the Miracle Worker. God, the Comforter and Sustainer. God, the Father, who had called him to preach the gospel of Jesus, the Son.

He thanked God aloud for the people awaiting baptism at Parana, at Arraias, Taguatinga, even in Campos Belos. He regretted his out-station work had caused him to spend so little time working in the place he had chosen to live. Still, God had blessed.

God, the One who removed the opposition. The priests' threats were no longer effective. One was even a friend. God, the Wonder Worker.

He was convinced God made his schedule. Last week he took

128

two of his girls, crowded in the back seat of the Piper, giggling, to enter high school. God was at work.

On the trip back, a young lady he had taken to the hospital two weeks earlier was ready to return. When he dropped her off, a new worker was ready to go to the school at Taguatinga. At Taguatinga there was a worker ready to join a new area outside Parana to hold a mission Bible school. Several people there wanted to talk to him about becoming Christians. At home there was a message that a new worker would meet him at Anapolis on March 29. He could take the worker to Arraias, go on to Corrente to get some documents he needed for the girls he had taken to the high school at Anapolis, and bring back a teacher from there to help him in his school at Campos Belos. All these things fell together like pieces of a puzzle, and they made Blonnye Foreman tremendously happy.

And health was good. A hundred and sixty pounds. It was like having the right air speed and the right altitude with a tail wind. Everything was as it should be. He thanked God. God, the Great Giver.

Tomorrow he would go to Anapolis and the next morning, the twenty-ninth, he would take the new worker to Arraias and make his trip to Corrente. It would be good to see his friends.

Today the faithful little plane was eating up distance toward a small village he had visited only once before. They had promised to make a landing strip and he had promised to come preach for them.

Blonnye Foreman eased back on the throttle and let the plane slip into a shallow glide toward a level area between two hills. One thing about this new preaching point—it would be easy to find from the air even in marginal weather. The altimeter slowly unwound: 4,000 feet; 3,500; 3,000; 2,000. Since the elevation in this area was about 1,800 feet, he judged he had about 200 feet of clearance as he eased the throttle forward to keep his air speed up when he leveled off. Now he could see the airstrip. A large group of people gathered around it. The realization of what he was able to do with that little plane never failed to give him a thrill. It gathered people better than a loudspeaker. His congregation was already there.

As he pulled over the field, however, his excitement dissipated before an unexpected problem. The field could not be over 300 yards long. He couldn't land and take off on such a short field. What could they have possibly been thinking about?

Moving the throttle forward full travel, he eased back on the stick and began a climbing turn to the left. Anxiously, he surveyed the field again as he moved in the opposite direction. At the same time he caught sight of the fire. He had asked them to have it burning as a wind sock when he came over. The smoke revealed a good sharp breeze traveling right down the strip. That's good. It should help him stop, and if it was still blowing when he took off, it would get him airborne quicker.

Perhaps he could make it. Pulling back on the throttle, he began another glide. Just above the trees he leveled off, gave it full throttle, and buzzed the strip. The people waved excitedly.

Stick back again. Another climbing turn. Yes, he would try. They had built that strip for him; they were expecting him; he would do it! He had not been flying in the bush all this time without learning something.

He extended his downwind, cut the throttle back, and turned slowly to line up with the little field. He was too high.

Stick left, right rudder. The plane began dropping quickly in a side slip. Yes, that would be about it. Air speed right. Hold it. The wind was good; it was holding directly down the field. Hold it. Brush coming up, but he would clear it. Now straighten it out. Left rudder. Stick right. Now back. Hold it. Hold it. Cut the throttle all the way. Stick back. Hold it, hold it, a bit more, now!

The air speed played out and the plane stalled just as it came over the edge of the runway. He stopped with a good hundred feet to spare. Taxiing up to the crowd he cut the throttle, turned off the gas, and slowly the propeller cranked to a halt. He felt good all over. It had been a perfect short field landing.

No sooner had the propeller stopped spinning than the people were all around the plane.

Quickly Blonnye opened the door, "Don't touch the plane! Don't touch the plane."

He grinned as he said it, hoping the sharpness of his voice would be moderated by the smile on his face.

"*Senhor* Foreman! *Senhor* Foreman! You came as you said you would. I have told the people you would come. Some of them did not believe me, but I told them.

"I said, '*Senhor* Foreman will come.' "

"Yes, I remembered my promise," said Blonnye, "and I see you have kept yours," indicating the field. No use telling them how totally inadequate it was. He could suggest lengthening it at a later time.

By nightfall, Blonnye was exhausted. He preached to two large crowds and there were several people to baptize. He would need to organize a church there before too long.

Blonnye had accepted the hospitality of his friends and now he had a few moments to himself. He decided to write a letter to his friends back home, the J. M. Sibleys. How good God was to preserve his friends. The Sibleys, the Moons, the Moores, Ruby Atwood—people who had supported him with money and prayers when he had come out to Brazil twenty-six years before, who still wrote him faithfully and prayed for him daily. And that brought another face to mind. But he had better write Sibley.

The letter was not as long as he knew it should be, but in it he shared a bit of the progress he had made in recent weeks, the usefulness of the plane, the day's events. He finished, sealed the letter, and decided he would mail it when he got to Anapolis the next day. It was a good kind of weariness that delivered him into an immediately sound sleep.

The next day Blonnye was relieved to see the wind still strong and still right down the runway. Dragging the plane all the way up to the end of the runway, he stuck the tail between two large bushes beyond the end of the runway to get all the run he could. Carefully, he picked up rocks and other debris lying around the plane. This would keep the propeller from kicking things back into the fuselage. Waving good-bye to his friends, he started the motor and climbed into the plane. He revved it up to full throttle before he released the brakes and began his take-off roll. Holding the stick back, he kept the tail down, and soon the plane broke ground. He lowered the nose slightly to build up the air speed and then applied back pressure again. The bush at the end of the strip passed under his wheels. No sweat. He climbed out sharply, knowing it would be an impossible place to navigate without that uniquely favoring wind.

Three hours later he landed at Anapolis and arranged for the servicing of his plane. A friend took him to see about his girls. No use worrying Musgrave at Goiania. He had seen him last week. He liked the young missionary and was grateful for his friendship and support. Sometimes he would fly low over Goiania and buzz the missionary's house when he needed his help. Musgrave, if at home, would come out, wave to him, and then meet him at the field in the International.

Musgrave was a good preacher, too. He and Blonnye had taken an extended preaching trip together which had been highly successful. Musgrave was more methodical and gave greater attention to detail than he, Blonnye, did. Blonnye felt now and then that Musgrave did not quite approve of his helter-skelter way of doing things, but he knew the young missionary liked him, and that made him feel good.

The girls were well settled. A lot of missionaries had not understood his attachment to the orphanage. The Mission Board had questioned him when he moved it to Campos Belos. Most of the support he had had to find himself, and the buildings were in his own name. He knew the Board did not totally approve of that either, but . . . He thought of how God had so providentially led him to open the orphanage. He had not only been able to give the children a good home, but through God's guiding hand they became able teachers to help him in the work throughout Goiania. Who would ever have thought when he began the orphanage that he was growing his own workers for a future day?

He was up early the next morning. A quick glance at his calendar wristwatch indicated the twenty-ninth of March. If he got moving now, he should be able to get the plane serviced and loaded and in the air about 6:45 A.M.

The weather was good in Anapolis, but the weather people told him there was a front somewhere to the north. He was supposed to pick up a worker at Formosa, but he decided to call and have someone tell the worker to go on to Arraias by commercial plane. He could pick him up there. This would allow Blonnye to fly straight north between the two mountain ranges, following the river through the Serra Dourada if the weather got too poor. Too, if his compass became a problem—it still was not functioning properly—he could follow the river north until he reached the familiar territory west of Campos Belos. He could find his way in there from any altitude.

"*Bom-dia, Senhor* Foreman." The friendly watchman—sometimes mechanic at Anapolis greeted Blonnye as he prepared his airplane for the morning flight. "It is a pretty day for flying."

"Yes, it is pretty here," replied Blonnye, "but they tell me it's going to get nasty north of here."

"So, you stay here another day?" the mechanic asked, smiling.

"No," said Blonnye, "I believe I can make my way through it. I'm an old hand at this business."

"*Sim.* You fly this country just about as much as anybody."

"How about propping the plane for me?" asked Blonnye.

"Surely."

Blonnye climbed into the front seat of the Super Cub and strapped himself in. No sunglasses. Oh, well, he'd be under clouds pretty soon and wouldn't need them.

"Contact," the boy yelled.

"Contact," Blonnye replied.

The plane caught on the first effort. Blonnye eased the throttle forward slowly, noting with satisfaction that the engine was running smoothly. He needed a ring job now; it was using more and more oil, but compression was good and he realized the advice he had received on buying a Super Cub instead of some other airplane had proved sound. Maintenance costs were below anything he had hoped for. The plane handled like a dream.

Waving a farewell to the smiling mechanic, he taxied to the end of the strip, whipped the nose around into the wind, said a brief prayer, and eased the throttle forward.

Blonnye leveled off at 4,000 feet as he climbed out of Anapolis. Below him he could see the road leading to Jaragua and could tell even from that altitude that the road descended sharply from the high plateau on which Anapolis was situated. The elevation there was 3,400 feet and at Jaragua it was only 2,001. On the other hand, the highest peak in the Serra Dourada, he remembered, was 4,400. At 4,000 he would be roughly 2,000 feet above the valley as he followed the Rio Tocantins. If the cloud level held high, however, it would not be necessary. He could cut north through the Serra Dourada.

As Blonnye passed the Anapolis plateau, the six or seven hundred feet behind him suddenly gave way to nearly 2,000 feet clearance. He clearly saw the weather front across the horizon. No real buildups, however. He decided it should be fairly stable atmosphere—clouds, and a few showers.

Over the little town of Jaragua, he turned toward the northeast. He noted wryly that his compass did not show that, but he confirmed the passage of the little town of Lagolandia under him. If he could get between the small peaks of the Serra Dourada, he felt he could still turn back to the Rio Tocantins on the other side. No use going that far out of the way. He would hold at 4,000 feet as long as he could.

Fifteen minutes later, Blonnye saw that 4,000 feet would not keep him below the leading layer of clouds. Throttling back, he began a slow descent. A thousand feet above the ground would still give him safety. The Serra Dourada was now above him, but he had plenty of clearance.

A few moments later he was past the Serra Dourada and skimming below darkening clouds. He heard the familiar peppering of rain almost before he saw the tiny rivulets of water running off his windshield. Throttling back even farther, he lost a little more altitude. Now he was under it again.

He knew he should turn back to the west and intercept the Rio Tocantins. There, if he held that heading for a few minutes, he would intercept the river. Then, no matter what the clouds did, he could find his way out.

For a moment things stabilized and Blonnye had a chance to think. How many times had he been in situations like this, aware he was pushing into weather that he probably should not attempt. Yet, he had always been able to make his way through. Really, there had never been a serious moment. Perhaps the time with Gene Wise when he flew the plane to Goias had been the most difficult episode.

He knew Gene would not approve of his pushing on into this front. Again cutting back the throttle, he let the plane drop some more. He had to stay under those swirling clouds. Again, rain peppered his windshield. The altimeter indicated about 2,500 feet now. As he looked out, he did not think he had that much clearance over the ground. That meant the pressure was probably dropping. He was probably moving into a low-pressure point. That would put the winds off his right wing tip.

He had learned to fly in a northern hemisphere where low pressures rotated counterclockwise and high pressures rotated clockwise. It had taken him awhile to understand that south of the equator it was just the opposite. Low pressures rotated clockwise and the high pressures rotated counterclockwise. At any rate, he could pretty well tell the wind component by the way he was traveling across the ground. He had a pretty good wind off his right wing.

With a little bit of luck he could make Arraias in another hour. He would land, take on gas, and pick up his worker. He could drop the worker off at Taguatinga and still make Corrente by nightfall— if the weather would give him a break.

He hated to hold this westerly bearing because it was taking him away from his destination, but he would feel better once he had the river beneath him.

Straining to the left, then to the right, Blonnye struggled to glimpse the river. Ah, there it is! Winding and turning as it did, it would be hard to follow at a low altitude.

He turned to what he assumed was a more northerly direction, but he had to get down still lower. He decided to fly on the east side of the river because he knew the river moved close to the mountains on the west. While they did not have peaks as high as the Serra Dourada, there were more of them.

Beginning to feel the tension of the trip, Blonnye strained forward to anticipate the river's turns. He knew it turned sharply to the east and then back to the north. Rain again peppered the windshield and forward visibility was almost nil. He held the little plane steady. He fought a growing sense of panic and focused on his instruments. Keep the needle straight and that will keep the wings level. Keep the air speed constant and that keeps the nose in the right attitude and makes it easier to hold altitude. . . .

He emerged from the small shower, but the clouds were getting lower. Reluctantly, he descended even farther. How much clearance now? About 300 feet he guessed. Oops! There was the bend to the east. Through the mist he could see one of the mountains. Stick to the right. Right rudder. Coordinate the turn. There, he had it. Now he was moving back to the east into the valley.

The river would swing north again long before there was any chance of coming up against the eastern mountain range. The mountains bracketed that section of the Rio Tocantins.

For a few moments Blonnye sang. He loved to sing and God had allowed him to use it to good advantage. The little pump organ now at Parana had been carried by mule back and airplane all over central Goias, and Blonnye had gradually widened his repertoire until he could sing and entertain a group for a couple of hours at one time—allowing for encores, of course.

Every now and then Blonnye wondered what kind of ministry he would have had if he had stayed in the States. What if he had let all the voices that had counseled him to wait until the Board could support him cause him to stay in the States? Would he have taken a pastorate? Would he then have gotten a larger one and followed that with still a larger one? Would he have married HER and had a family? Could he have served on committees and denominational programs and given prayers at Kiwanis Club luncheons?

It was funny, but he could not visualize himself as anything other than what he had been—a pioneer mission teacher and preacher, a muleteer on back trails in Brazil. An agriculturalist, a pilot, a preacher, a singer, a jackleg doctor, a counselor, a daddy to orphans, an old bachelor.

Blonnye banked the plane to keep sight of the river under him. Now where'd the river go? He banked the plane to the right. No river. Nothing but brush and rock. Slowly he banked to the left. Where in the world did the river go? Did he miss the turn to the north? He looked at his compass. It was no help at all. On the other hand, if he missed the northern turn and kept straight ahead, he would soon be in trouble in some of the roughest mountains in Goias.

He banked the plane to the left for what he estimated was about 90 degrees and held it there. Rain peppered the plexiglass. He had to throttle back to get under the clouds again. He was really too low for safety's sake. If something should happen to his engine now, he would have no time to select a place to go down.

The ground began to rise ahead of him. Surely he could not be moving into those mountains. The turbulence was increasing. He realized the front was more unstable than he had thought. *Which way was the wind from?* Maybe that would help. But he was too close to the ground to discern drift—especially with the turbulence. The problem now was to keep the plane off the ground and under the clouds. The rain came harder.

That river must be farther to the left. The ground was still rising. He must be going toward the mountains. Again he banked. He would hold it for fifteen minutes. He looked at his watch. No sooner had he looked back and leveled his wings, which were increasingly difficult to keep parallel to the ground, than he realized he had not really seen what his watch indicated. He looked back again.

As Blonnye peered through the peppering rain he admitted to himself he was lost. He reached for his map and tried to fold it over his knee. As he did, the plane slipped off to the right and the ground rose alarmingly. He decided to turn left again. He had no idea whether he had gone 180 degrees or farther. He looked at the map. Actually it was of no help; he knew all these things. What he had to find was some landmark.

There! There is the river! He turned toward it. Almost as soon as he crossed it, he realized it was not the river but a tributary. Which way was it going? He guessed, and turned to the right. Evidently he had overflown the river and not seen it.

He flew about ten minutes down the tributary before it began to wind in and out of rocky ground and Blonnye knew he was following it in the wrong direction. He would turn back.

He made a slow circle and had to descend again because of the clouds. Heavy rain pelted the plane, and for a moment he was totally enveloped in a cloud. When he emerged, he glanced at his watch. He had been flying for nearly three hours. That left him about two hours flying time—more than enough to get to Arraias if he could figure out which way to go.

What happened to the creek he had been following? It was gone. Again a cloud enveloped him. Panic gripped him, and he shoved the stick forward. He dropped immediately out of the cloud, but there was the ground rising up sharply. He pulled back. The scream of the wind along the wings reminded him he was putting a terrible stress on the plane. He tried to loosen his sweaty grip. "Lord, I got myself into this; you're going to have to get me out. Lord, I trust thee. Lord, I'm in thy hands."

He tried to relax. He would hold that heading. What he needed was to remain calm. If worse came to worst, he could always land. As he looked down at the rocky, broken ground under him, he realized that would be a dangerous operation, however. The chances of landing his plane in one piece were pretty remote. He could probably walk away from it, but then he would have a long walk.

A hill loomed up directly ahead. What now? Surely he had not crossed the river again. The hill looked more like what he had passed earlier in the morning in the Serra Dourada.

There, right under him—a ranch house! He flew over and strained to see. Two men were working in a corral near the house. Turn now. Go back by. That's the place to get down and wait out the weather. *Surely I can find an open place to land. . . .*

Blonnye banked the plane and again pushed the stick forward as another cloud threatened to envelop him.

There is the ranch house again. There are the men. But where could he land? Were they waving? Were they pointing? Were they pointing toward an airstrip or a place to land? Turn again.

The clouds had him. He shoved the nose down again and then in panic pulled back hard as a hill loomed up in front of him. *Turn! Turn! Get back over the ranch house!*

Mountains loomed up. He turned to the left. No good. He turned back to the right. The mountains again. He turned to the left. He was in a box canyon. There was not room enough to turn around.

A cloud grabbed him. Altitude. He had to climb through it. No other choice. He shoved the throttle forward and eased back on the stick. Immediately he was in the clouds and all vision was gone.

Keep the needle centered. Keep enough air speed. Climb out on top like he did with Gene. When he got on top he could find a hole to get through later on. Get above those mountains. The altimeter indicated a slow climb—2,500; 3,000. It faltered. Back to 2,900, back to 2,800. Keep the needle centered. It kept slipping off to the left. *Keep it centered. . . .*

Sheer panic grabbed Blonnye as he struggled to understand what was happening. He did not have instrument training. He was in over his head. *Keep trying. Don't give up.*

The needle centered. But wind was screaming across the plexiglass surrounding him. To his horror he realized his air speed was building up fast—140 miles an hour. Altitude was down to 2,600. Center the needle. It was back to the left. Pull back on the stick. Speed dropping down too low. He would stall. Drop the nose. Altitude 2,600. Hold it. He could see the ground. *Straighten up the wing!* Too late.

As if he were an onlooker and not a participant, Blonnye saw the wing catch the rugged rock of the protruding hill. It seemed to rip the controls right out of his hand. Then, in instantaneous sequence, it all came through the windshield.

17
April 19, 1955
5:00 A.M.

(JAMES MUSGRAVE)

Blonnye Holmes Foreman. The words stood out starkly and irrefutably. Musgrave's hands trembled as he held the identification card in the light. The weeks of tension and anxiety had come to fruition. The worst had come true. Blonnye was dead.

"I am so sorry for your friend," the rancher said. "Perhaps it would help you to know he must have died instantly. The plane was turned over and burned partially, but the body was still inside. It looked as if a piece of the wing, or something, had been driven directly through the head." The man placed a finger between his eyes to indicate the direction the piece of wreckage had penetrated the missionary's forehead. "He knew no pain, *senhor*."

Musgrave looked at him, trying to comprehend what he was saying. Then as he realized the man was trying to comfort him with the assurance Blonnye had not suffered. His fears that Blonnye had been lying trapped in the wreckage while they waited were unfounded. It had been all over for Blonnye in an instant.

The lieutenant spoke up. "How far is the wreckage?"

"It is about six miles," the rancher replied. We can walk it from here if you like."

A gray dawn was overcoming the darkness of the night.

"Yes," Jim said, "we'd better go up there."

141

Soon the men were walking single file after the rancher, who had put on a large leather hat and pulled heavy boots over his leather trousers. He was much better equipped for the rugged country than they were, Jim thought, wincing as he hit his ankle on a heavy piece of rock in the poor light of the early dawn.

The sky to the east was turning into a distinct pink, and with it the ruggedness of the Serra Dourada was more evident. To his right Musgrave could see a high peak.

"That must be the 4,400-foot peak," he said to the lieutenant.

The lieutenant, very silent throughout all of this, looked up and nodded.

The grade steepened and soon all of them were breathing hard. Every now and then the rancher stopped and looked back to make sure the four visitors were still with him. Once he moved up a brush ravine and had to backtrack out of it.

"I am sorry," he said to his followers, "I have not come back up here since I buried the pilot. I do not like to visit the place. There is something very tragic about it."

No one said anything but dutifully followed the man as he backtracked, climbed laboriously out of the ravine, and followed a ridge of land that paralleled it.

The rancher, pulling ahead of them, stopped and waited for them to catch up. As they did, he turned and said, "There it is."

It was a barren, windswept piece of ground, a side of hill which Musgrave guessed loomed up unexpectedly before Blonnye. It was obvious the plane had hit with terrific impact. A wing was collapsed and folded across the cockpit. The motor was shoved back into the cockpit. The plane lay like a broken toy with only the tail assembly intact.

"It was on its back when I found it," said the rancher. "I had to turn it over to extract the man's body. It was a very difficult job because he had been there so long."

The rancher tried to speak tactfully as he sensed the depth of the sorrow felt by these men who had come to find their friend.

In the dreamlike light of the early dawn, they slowly approached the wreckage. About ten feet from the wreckage was a mound of rocks. The rancher had evidently piled them over it to keep animals from getting to it.

"I am afraid I could not dig very deep," the rancher said, when he noticed the direction of their gaze.

A crude cross sagged to one side from a pile of stones and the rancher quickly walked to it and tried to right it. It would not stay, however, so he found another stone and propped it up.

The five men stood looking at the rocky grave. Slowly Jim Musgrave's numbed thoughts comprehended the situation. The search for Blonnye Foreman was over. He hardly noticed Pastor Elias walk up and stand beside him until the pastor began to read solemnly from his New Testament. He read slowly and haltingly.

Musgrave looked at the group of men. The pastor was crying. So was Brother Adistio. The lieutenant had removed his hat and was holding it across his chest, looking down at the grave.

As Pastor Elias read, Musgrave looked at the sky around him. There were no clouds. The gray had given way to a bright blue and the sun promised a beautiful, bright day.

Right here everything had ended. Blonnye's missionary ministry was over. His pioneering in Goias was over. His preaching and singing and traveling were over. They would not hear him laugh again. Jim would not hear again the sound of the small plane buzzing him to come to the airport. On this rocky hill Blonnye Foreman had finished his earthly pilgrimage.

After Pastor Elias finished reading, the men went about gathering anything they thought would be helpful in winding up the investigation. Musgrave found a piece of metal with the prefix PTARM. "Blonnye's 'right arm,' " he said aloud.

"What's that?" asked the lieutenant, trying to read a burned piece of paper.

"Nothing," said Musgrave, "just talking to myself."

"Shall we try to recover Blonnye's body?" the pastor asked.

The lieutenant spoke up. "No, it is against the law to move a man's body without a court order. We will have to leave him here for the time being."

"It is only his body that is here," said Brother Adistio. "Blonnye is with the Lord."

The lieutenant looked at Adistio strangely and then went back to the task of picking up evidence that might be helpful.

The sun was full in the sky when the five men stopped again at the grave and Jim Musgrave led them in a prayer. Then, single file, they started down the mountain. Musgrave trailed the group, and as they started over the rise that would take them out of sight of the wreckage, he turned around and looked back at the scene once more.

Had he expected it all to change miraculously? Had he expected the wreckage not to be there, the rocky grave with its pathetic little cross to somehow dissolve into a figment of his imagination? Whatever he had expected, reality was what he saw. The crumbled remains of the plane. The little grave so poignantly positioned beside it. The rugged terrain. The high peak of the Serra Dourada looking down dispassionately from the west.

But was that all the reality? In the focus of faith was not it equally real that at this spot Blonnye had gone to meet the Lord he had served so faithfully? Was it not reality, also, that at the moment in time when his plane had struck this mountain, Blonnye had entered into the presence of God? Into a glad reunion with loved ones and friends with whom he had shared the faith of Christ?

Sunlight now bathed the whole area and, in the context of these thoughts, reality was not so grim, the wreckage not so harsh, the little grave not at all pathetic. This was where a fine and good man—a man who had, to the best of his ability, lived as he thought God would have him live—had finished his pilgrimage. Jim Musgrave turned and hurried after the others. He did not look back again.